the Dublin Pubspotter's guide

Photo by John Brady

About the author

I am from Fairview, Dublin and now live between Ireland's capital city and London, where I drive a black London licensed cab. I went to St Josephs (Joey's) School, Fairview, Dublin 3. While I was still at school I started work as a van helper, delivering fruit and vegetables to shops round Dublin. I went on to drive an egg van delivering eggs to Dublin and surrounding counties to hospitals and supermarkets. This earned me the name, The Egg Man. I also worked part-time in pubs in Dublin. My father and my uncle also worked in Dublin pubs. In London in the early 1980s I worked in pubs, eventually managing one myself in London's West End. My work as a London cabbie began in the mid-1990s and continues to this day. Learning how to be a licensed London cab driver involved studying what is commonly known as 'The Knowledge' of London. This course involved riding a moped all around the city, learning routes in every direction and memorising every place of importance. I was regularly tested on my knowledge and then one day, somewhere in the region of three years from when I commenced, I received my green badge and a job for life.

Mac Moloney, October 2012

the Dublin Pubspotter's guide

Mac Moloney

A. & A. Farmar

British Library Cataloguing in Publications Data

A CIP catalogue record for this book is available from the British Library.

ISBN: 978-1-906353-32-2

First published in 2012 by A. & A. Farmar Ltd, 78 Ranelagh Village, Dublin 6, Ireland
Tel 353 1 496 3625 Email afarmar@iol.ie website www.aafarmar.ie

Typeset and designed by DTP Workshops

Printed and bound by GraphyCems

POSTCODE GUIDE

This guide is divided into seven sections, covering four city and suburban areas with postcodes and three county areas. Postcode areas with odd numbers are north of the river Liffey (with the exception of the Phoenix Park, which is in Dublin 8), even numbers are south of the Liffey

North city centre

Dublin 1: City centre, north of the Liffey.

South city centre

Dublin 2: City centre south of the Liffey.

Dublin North suburbs

Dublin 3: Ballybough, North Strand, Clonliffe, Clontarf, Dollymount, East Wall, Fairview, most of Killester and Marino.

Dublin 5: most of Artane, Coolock (other parts of Coolock are in Dublin 13 and 17), Harmonstown, Kilbarrack, Raheny and Edenmore.

Dublin 7: Smithfield, Cabra, Grangegorman, Phibsborough, Ashtown and Stoneybatter.

Dublin 9: Beaumont, Drumcondra, part of Glasnevin, Santry, Whitehall, Donnycarney and parts of Ballymun.

Dublin 11: Finglas, Meakstown, most of Glasnevin and most of Ballymun.

Dublin 13: Bayside, Baldoyle, Donaghmede, Portmarnock, Sutton and the Ayrfield part of Coolock.

Dublin 15: Castleknock, Carpenterstown, Blanchardstown, Clonsilla, Coolmine, Corduff, Mulhuddart and Tyrellstown.

Dublin 17: Balgriffin, most of Coolock (apart from Ayrfield which is in Dublin 13), Clonshaugh, Corballis, Ballygall, Priorswood, Darndale, Northern Cross and Clarehall.

Dublin South suburbs

Dublin 4: Ballsbridge, Donnybrook, Belfield, Irishtown, Ringsend and Sandymount.

Dublin 6: Milltown, Ranelagh, Rathmines, Dartry and Rathgar.

Dublin 6W: Harold's Cross, Kimmage, Templeogue and Terenure.

Dublin 8: Phoenix Park, Kilmainham, Portobello, South Circular Road, Dolphin's Barn, The Coombe, Rialto, The Liberties, Inchicore, and Islandbridge.

Dublin 10: Ballyfermot.

Dublin 12: Bluebell, Crumlin, Drimnagh, Perrystown and Walkinstown.

Dublin 14: Churchtown, Clonskeagh, Dundrum, Goatstown, Rathfarnham and Windy Arbour.

Dublin 16: Ballinteer, Knocklyon, Balally and Rockbrook.

Dublin 18: Cabinteely, Cornelscourt, Carrickmines, Foxrock, Kilternan, Sandyford and Stepaside.

Dublin 20: Chapelizod and Palmerstown.

Dublin 22: Clondalkin and Liffey Valley.

Dublin 24: Firhouse, Jobstown and Tallaght.

North County Dublin

The Naul, Balscadden, Balbriggan, Balrothery, Ballyboughal, Oldtown, Skerries, Lusk, Rush, Donabate, Howth, Garristown, Kinsealy, Cloghran, Swords, Malahide and Collinstown.

South County Dublin

Glencullen, Leopardstown, Booterstown, Stillorgan, Kilmacud, Goatstown, Mount Merrion, Blackrock, Monkstown, Dún Laoghaire, Deansgrange, Kill of the Grange, Glasthule, Sandycove, Dalkey, Killiney, Loughlinstown, Ballybrack and Shankill.

West County Dublin

Brittas, ,Hazelhatch, Lucan, Finnstown, Newcastle, Rathcoole and Saggart.

My late father Con Moloney who worked in some of Dublin's famous pubs was a good judge of people. He often used a great phrase about people who liked many drinks: 'That fellow is very fond of having his elbow on the mahogany.'

I once asked him did he think I was like that and he said 'No, son, you're ok.'

Con was still with us when I started the Dublin Pubspotter's Guide tour. He would have been very proud of me today now that this book has been published.

Please note

- Pubs' opening days and times may have changed since the data in this book was compiled. Similarly, some places which previously served food may no longer do so, whereas others may have begun to serve food to boost their takings.
- Entertainment in pubs takes many forms, from traditional music sessions to bingo and singalongs. Some pubs which used to offer entertainment no longer do so whereas others have started to put on events to attract customers. If you are interested in a particular type of entertainment it is a good idea to contact the pub to check what is on offer.
- Some of the entries about pubs which have a large selection of whiskeys refer to the Irish Whiskey Trail—irelandwhiskeytrail.com—which is a guide to Ireland's distilleries, best whiskey pubs, hotel and golf club bars.

You can keep a record of the pubs you visit by filling in the date of your visit in the space provided in each pub entry in this guide: _ _/_ _/**20**_ _

Contents

Introduction

Hello! Thank you for your interest in my book which must be Dublin's largest documented pub crawl. For nearly ten years I have been researching this project, which means that I have travelled all over Dublin city and county using every form of public transport and getting friends to drive me around as well. I have kept a receipt for a drink for every place as proof I was there. Collecting these was good fun, because asking the bar server for a receipt was considered an unusual request, and they often thought I was a 'pub spy' or 'Guinness tester'. I would get some funny looks and many would repeat, 'A receipt?' I can now say I have had a pint of Guinness in every pub that I could find in Dublin, meeting many people and making many friends on the way. It took me the equivalent of eleven barrels of Guinness to have a pint in every pub in Dublin (968 pints!). For me this is my own 'Guinness record'.

I believe that having been in every pub at least four times, I have memorised the interiors so well that if I was blindfolded and brought to any pub listed in this book, I could name it and tell you interesting facts and figures about it.

Photographing all the pubs became a large part of this book. I have learned a lot about photography over the last few years and can now understand a photographer's frustration, for example, arriving at a pub when the light is perfect but a vehicle or scaffolding is blocking the shot! I am also aware that pubs never stop changing their appearances. On my return to establishments I would often find that many had changed their names or exterior wall colour and so I would have to get out my trusty camera again and replace the old image with a new one.

The idea for this book started off from a pub crawl. While in a pub I overheard people talking and reminiscing about pubs. A recurring question was, 'Were you ever in that place, and what does it look like now?' The subject of pubs often led to conversations about times past and how a place had changed, or about people who had moved away.

As a young lad I used to visit pubs all over Ireland with friends. On our travels we would see how many pubs were in a town and then we would try to visit every establishment in the area. This became my idea for Dublin, except of course, this was a much bigger area. I greatly enjoyed touring around Dublin as its pubs gave me a way of learning about my city. The journey evolved from doing a pub crawl on my own to an obsession that included trying to find as many little-known and out-of-the-way pubs as I could.

Most people who have written books on pubs in Dublin city have picked only the oldest or those that have a lot of history attached to them. I have included not only these but all the other pubs in this great city of Dublin. Many of these other pubs also offer fascinating stories and information and I hope you'll enjoy reading about them and checking out their images.

Bus-, plane- and trainspotting are regular hobbies for many enthusiasts. Generally, those who practise these activities are called 'anoraks' as they are out in all weathers checking out their subjects. I want to add pubspotting to the list.

With pubspotting you can have a beverage in a nice warm pub without needing an anorak! Many people here in Ireland go on pub crawls regularly but don't catalogue the pubs they went to. If you consider taking up pubspotting this book will be a great help as you can mark and date each pub you visit in your copy of *The Dublin Pubspotter's Guide*.in the space provided next to each entry: **_ _/_ _/20_ _**. If you visit ten establishments a week it will take you two years to visit every pub and hotel bar in Dublin, so take your time while enjoying your journey! I recommend that you bring your book along and place it on the bar counter as I believe it will be a good conversation starter.

Over my years of researching this book I have found that around two establishments per week close, reopen under a different name, change name and/or appearance, and start or stop offering food or entertainment. I have tried to keep up-to-date with all these changes to the best of my ability, but I am aware that more changes have occurred since I completed my research in August 2012. I am also aware that I may have missed a few details in various pubs. As far as I am aware I have found all of the pubs in Dublin. I have included some pubs that are currently closed because they may well reopen in the future. If I have missed yours or if you know of a place I have overlooked, please contact me and I will visit the establishment to record its details for future use. I welcome information from any publican or member of the public. Please send your comments and suggestions to me at dublinpubspottersguide@gmail.com or text to 087 191 7960. I hope to see a copy of this book in every pub in Dublin and intend to revisit all the pubs over the next few years so that I can update my records and bring out a revised edition. This will make the current volume a history book and hopefully, in time, a collector's item.

A brief history of pubs

Pubs have been around for centuries, starting as shebeens or inns. They have changed a lot from smoke-filled rooms with sawdust on the floor to places where you can relax in comfortable surroundings. In the past when men got together in a pub they would be loud and use choice language. This was permitted as no women were present—with the exception of the licensee's wife. Women were not served in public houses until the mid-1900s and this brought the introduction of the snug and then the lounge. A snug is a small sectioned-off area of a pub and was at one time the only place where women could have a drink. They were also used by patrons who didn't want to be seen in the public bar. Lounges had carpets and usually table service and drinks were usually more expensive to cover this luxury. Nowadays, of course, the bar and lounge areas have both men and women drinking together.

Pubs were usually owned by private individuals and had their names on signs over the door outside, for example, 'Moloney's'. However, pubs also are given names such as 'The Barrel and Bottle Inn'. Most of these pubs are handed down to a family member who continues the business.

A pub is the sitting room of the owner of the pub and he is your host. As long as you keep to the house rules you can stay but if you step out of line you are ousted for a time. This is known as being 'barred'.

Local pubs are a great place to go to mix with friends. Every time I return home from London I look forward to visiting my local and there are many regulars there I enjoy talking to over a couple of pints. It is a great way to end my day.

An interesting observation is that you can visit a pub, meet a great group of lads, and have a great chat and craic with them. When you return another time none of these lads may be around but there will usually be someone you can talk to. Pubs are created by the customers and they make the atmosphere. For example, most pubs follow sport and these sports bars often have multiple televisions showing the day's various events.

Different types of bars and pubs

Shebeens
Shebeens were originally bars where alcoholic drinks were sold without a licence. The word 'shebeen' comes from the Irish *sibín*, meaning 'illicit whiskey'.

Inns
Inns originated from places which provided accommodation, food and drink to travellers. They were often situated in the country or along highways. In the past inns also had stables where horses and other animals could be fed and watered.

Early houses
There are around a dozen early houses in Dublin. They are usually situated near a port or market like the Dublin City Council fruit and vegetable market. This allows all-night workers to have a beverage after work. These pubs can open as early as 7 a.m. but some do not open until later in the morning. The owners/managers use their discretion as to whom they let in, as revellers from the previous night who are still in a party mood may be too loud and disruptive. Often a code, such as ringing a hidden doorbell or tapping on a window, will allow you to enter. It is a fun thing to go to some of these pubs in the morning and to get a bus home about midday. The only other places where you can get an early drink are hotels when you are a resident, an airport when you are airside (the area beyond security checks and passport and customs control), or on board a ferry.

Hotel bars
Some hotels are for residents only but the larger ones have great bars where anyone can visit and have a drink in a relaxed atmosphere with background music playing. They are also places where you can get away from everything and relax with a book or a paper.

Restaurant bars
Some restaurants call themselves bars, whereas in fact they are actually holding areas until your table is ready. My understanding of the term is that it is a bar if you can have drinks without food and there are bar stools. If there are only table seating areas, in this case the venue usually has a restaurant licence.

Nightclubs
There are many nightclubs throughout Dublin. These are mostly open at weekends but some in the city centre open during the week as well. Usually they open around 10 p.m. and close in the early morning. Many clubs are connected to hotels or pubs—these are the only one included in this guide.

Pub opening times
Most pubs open at 10.30 a.m. and close at 11.30 p.m. Mondays to Thursdays, 10.30 a.m. to 12.30 a.m. Fridays and Saturdays and 12.30 p.m. to 11.30 p.m. on Sundays. Pubs open every day with the exception of Christmas Day and Good Friday. Nightclubs open at various times, and stop serving drink at 2.30 a.m.

Golf and other sports clubs
There are many golf and other sports clubs around Dublin, some of which are like traditional local pubs. I have been in many but I gave up going to them when some insisted that I wear a jacket and tie. It is possible to drink in most of these clubs without being a member. Officially, however, to be allowed to drink in a club you should be a member or be with a member.

Wine bars
There are many wine bars that only serve wine as well as food. However, some also have a small selection of bottled beer. I have visited many of these and in my opinion they do not fit the category of 'public house', so they are not listed in this book.

Acknowledgements

I would like to thank John Brady, an old school friend who helped me all the way through this book. When I first started out I was using a pen and paper. I soon discovered a computer was needed, but I had no technical know-how. John has lots of computer experience and was a great teacher. Later, when I decided to photograph all the pubs, John helped me get started with a digital camera. We went on a few trips to various pubs where he showed me the basics of taking pictures. John also has a great knowledge of Dublin and has driven me all around the city and county. He is not a drinker, which meant I could have a pint and he would drive me from pub to pub.

I would also like to thank Mark Sedgwick, FIPF EFIAP ESFIAP and former President of the Irish Photographic Federation who edited my pictures, while pointing out my many mistakes. Mark's great knowledge of photography really helped me with my own work. This meant I often returned to pubs for reshoots as I was able to take better pictures over time. Mark told me how to stand and hold the camera and what settings to use. When I look back on my work pre Mark's help, I can clearly see how far I've come. Thank you, Mark, you are a gentleman. His website is www.theremarkableimage.com.

I would like to thank my sisters Angela, Cathy and Noreen who helped me with my research. Thanks for all your kindness and patience over a long period of time!

I would like to thank Nicola Sedgwick who worked with me on editing the book and also with my research. I was never one for English at school, and Nicola taught me how to make a sentence flow and where to put a full stop.

I would like to thank the many publicans and their staff who gave me information. I would particularly like to thank the management and staff of P. J. Branagan's Pub in the Tara Towers Hotel, where Nicola and I spent a lot of time working on this book.

I would like to thank Tony and Anna Farmar of A. & A. Farmar for taking me on and giving me great encouragement. I would like to thank Dave Cullen of DTP Workshops for creating a great layout for the book.

I would like to thank my sister Mary and her husband Terence who gave me great encouragement along the way.

I would like to thank everyone who toured Dublin's pubs with me: Paul Blanche, fellow cab driver and brother-in-law; Áine Doherty; Kevin Foley, fellow cab driver, also known as Galway Kev; the cockney Pat from Kerry; John Glasheen (Glash), my brother-in-law; my good friend Lillian; Ann McDonald; Mick O'Mahoney and Ann T.

Lastly, my apologies to anyone I may have inadvertently omitted.

Mac Moloney, Dublin, October 2012

North City Centre

Most of the north inner city, with its rich history, is in the Dublin 1 postal code area.

O'Connell Street is Dublin City's main street. It was known as Sackville Street until 1924, when it was renamed in honour of Daniel O'Connell, the Irish nationalist leader. His statue, called the O'Connell Memorial, stands at the lower end of the street. The street is also home to the famous Gresham Hotel and Clerys Department Store. The GPO (General Post Office) is situated halfway down O'Connell Street. It was one of the last great Georgian public buildings to be erected in Dublin. During the Easter Rising of 1916, the GPO was the headquarters of the uprising's leaders. The marks left by bullets during the Rising can still be seen on the columns outside the building. The Spire of Dublin (official title 'Monument of Light') is a pin-like stainless steel monument 121.1 metres high, located on the site of the former Nelson's Pillar on O'Connell Street. It can be seen across Dublin at night.

On Marlborough Street, just off O'Connell Street to the east, you can find St Mary's Pro-Cathedral. It is the cathedral of the Roman Catholic Archdiocese of Dublin. The church is well-known for its Palestrina Boys Choir.

Henry Street, off O'Connell Street to the west, is one of Dublin's two most-travelled shopping streets, the other being Grafton Street. It is home to the Ilac and Jervis Street Shopping Centres, department stores and numerous smaller outlets.

The national theatre of Ireland, the Abbey Theatre, is located on Abbey Street. It is closely associated with many renowned Irish playwrights and actors.

Parnell Square is home to the following features:

- The Hugh Lane Gallery, also called the Municipal Gallery of Modern Art.
- The Dublin Writers Museum, a few doors up from the gallery, with exhibitions relating to Irish writers who have made an important contribution to Irish and international literature.
- The Garden of Remembrance, at the northern end of Parnell Square. It is dedicated to the men and women who died in pursuit of Irish freedom. This is where Queen Elizabeth II began her famous state visit to Ireland in 2011.
- The Gate Theatre, founded in 1928 by Hilton Edwards and Micheál Mac Liammóir.
- The Rotunda Hospital, which is one of the three main maternity hospitals in Dublin.

Mountjoy Square, one of five Georgian squares in Dublin, has been home to many of Dublin's most prominent people, including James Joyce, Sean O'Casey, and W.B. Yeats. Most of the Oscar-winning film *Once* was made here.

The Ha'penny Bridge, close to O'Connell Bridge, is a pedestrian bridge spanning the River Liffey. Its name derived from a time in the past when a ha'penny toll was charged from anyone crossing it.

The O2 is a large theatre located at North Wall Quay. It was built on the site of the former Point Theatre. Many music events have been staged here.

The IFSC (International Financial Services Centre) is a major financial services centre situated in North Wall. The centre has now been extended and includes office accommodation, educational institutions, executive housing and shopping facilities.

Summerhill is a district just north of the Liffey comprising retail outlets, apartments and residential housing.

The Auld Triangle

28 Lower Dorset Street, Dublin 1
A traditional local pub close to Croke Park, a real 'characters' pub. It was once called Bush's and The Four Seasons. There is occasional entertainment.

_ _/_ _/20_ _

Bachelor Inn

31 Bachelors Walk, Dublin 1
(1) 873 1238
www.thebachelorinn.com
Known to its many locals as The Batch, this traditional city centre pub, 'The Home of Poets' Corner' was established in the 19th century. It was previously called O'Mara's. Food is served every day and there is regular entertainment.

_ _/_ _/20_ _

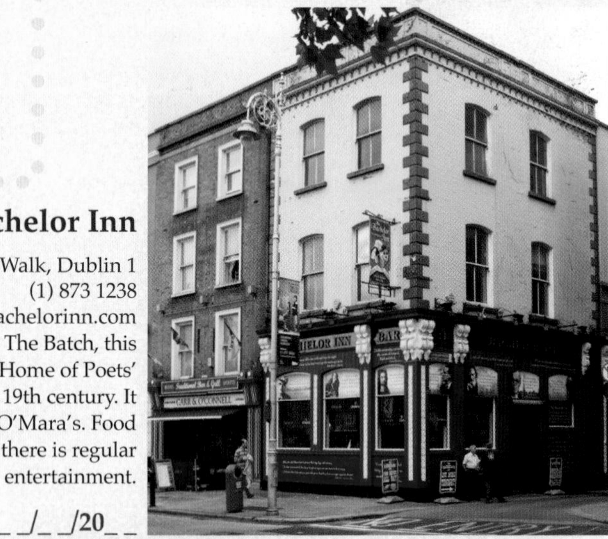

Barry's Hotel Bar

Barry's Hotel, 1–2 Great Denmark Street, Dublin 1
(1) 874 9407
barrys_hotel@eircom.net
A traditional bar 'in the heart of Dublin' opened by Mrs Barry in 1889. It was once home to The Tudor Rooms. Food is served every day.

_ _/_ _/20_ _

Aurora

72–73 Upper Dorset Street, Dublin 1
(1) 830 7929
www.theaurora.ie
A gastro pub, merging a classic Victorian bar with modern influences. Previously called The Cosy Bar and O'Neill's and often referred to as The Snug, it has traded as Aurora since 2006. Food is served every day and there is occasional entertainment.

_ _/_ _/20_ _

Belvedere Bar

The Belvedere Hotel, Great Denmark Street, Dublin 1
(1) 873 7721
info@belvederehotel.ie
www.belvederehoteldublin.com
This hotel bar is also called The Poet's Lounge. Food is served every day and there is regular entertainment. The hotel, which is near Parnell Square, was previously called The Comfort Inn Hotel.

_ _/_ _/20_ _

Bermingham's

111 Upper Dorset Street, Dublin 1
(1) 830 5083
A traditional local pub, one of those places in Dublin which never seems to change.

_ _/_ _/20_ _

The Big Tree Tavern

33–40 Lower Dorset Street, Dublin 1
(1) 855 3403
bigtree@fitzgeraldgroup.ie
www.bigtree.ie
Dating back to 1543 this traditional local pub close to Croke Park also houses Root's Nightclub. It was previously called McDonalds's Big Tree and The Rose Tavern. Opening times and days vary. The pub was renovated in late 2010, keeping some of its wonderful old historical features. It has an internal phone system with telephones on selected tables and walls, which allows you to dial a nearby table to flirt with your neighbour! There is regular entertainment.

_ _/_ _/20_ _

The Black Sheep

61–63 Capel Street, Dublin 1
(1) 873 0013
www.winefoodbeer.com
Promising 'Crafty beer, simple food' this modern city centre bar was previously called Barnstormer Rock Bar, The Blue Note, Deluxe, @ The Living Room, Mischief, Quinlan's, Tracey's, Yellow, and most recently Deluxe. It has traded as The Black Sheep since 2012.

_ _/_ _/20_ _

The Boar's Head

149 Capel Street, Dublin 1
(1) 872 3107
theboarshead@eircom.net
A traditional city centre pub which operates as an early house. Food is served every day and there is occasional entertainment.

_ _/_ _/20_ _

Bleecker Street

68 Upper Dorset Street, Dublin 1
(1) 804 4459
A café bar which opened in 2010. It was previously called Hourican's, The Old Brogue and more recently Jim Beam's All-American Bar. There is regular entertainment.

_ _/_ _/20_ _

Bodkins

57 Bolton Street, Dublin 1
(1) 873 0128
info@bodkinsbar.com
www.bodkinsbar.com
A traditional local pub opposite DIT Bolton Street and five minutes' walk from O'Connell Street. It was previously called The Yarn Hall, after Yarnhall Street which is at the side of the pub. Food is served every day.

_ _/_ _/20_ _

Bondi Beach Club

35 Lower Ormond Quay, Dublin 1
A bar and nightclub, previously named Zanzibar. This establishment is currently closed.

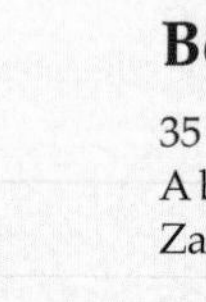

_ _/_ _/20_ _

Brannigan's

9 Cathedral Street, Dublin 1
(1) 874 0137
A traditional city centre pub established in 1909 just off O'Connell Street. Its previous names were The Goal Post and Madigan's. Food is served every day and there is regular entertainment.

_ _/_ _/20_ _

The Brew Dock

1 Amiens Street, Dublin 1
(1) 888 1842
www.winefoodbeer.com
Located opposite the IFSC, Busáras and Connolly Station this pub serves a large selection of craft beers. It was previously known as The Master Mariner and The Steering Wheel, and most recently as Kate's Cottage. The pub dates back to around 1840. Food is served every day.

_ _/_ _/20_ _

Briody's

97 Marlborough Street, Dublin 1
(1) 872 7016
Known to some of its regulars as The TV Shop this traditional city centre pub was established around 1900. A light snack menu is served.

_ _/_ _/20_ _

Burke's

47 Amiens Street, Dublin 1,
A great old Victorian-style pub, previously called Timlin's. This establishment is currently closed.

_ _/_ _/20_ _

Carr and O'Connell

30 Bachelors Walk, Dublin 1
(1) 874 5730
carrandoconnell@hotmail.com
A modern city centre pub, previously called Panama. Food is served every day and there is regular entertainment.

_ _/_ _/20_ _

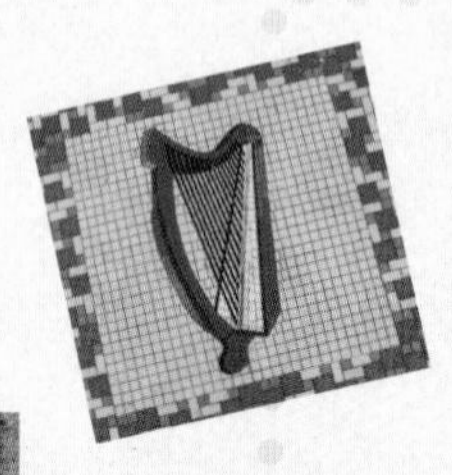

Castle Hotel Vaults Bar and Grill

Castle Hotel, 2–4 Great Denmark Street, Dublin 1, (1) 874 6949
info@castle-hotel.ie, www.castle-hotel.ie
An elegant Georgian hotel bar in the city centre. The hotel incorporates Walton's Hotel. Food is served every day and there is regular entertainment.

_ _/_ _/20_ _

Caulfield's Hotel Bar

Caulfield's Hotel, 18–19 Lower Dorset Street, Dublin 1
(1) 878 1550
caulfieldshotel@eircom.net
Food is served every day in this hotel bar and there is regular entertainment. The hotel is near the city centre.

_ _/_ _/20_ _

The Celt

81 Talbot Street, Dublin 1
(1) 878 8655
info@celticlodge.ie leboncrubeen@gmail.com
www.thecelt.ie
An old world traditional Irish pub in the city centre, connected to The Celtic Lodge Guest House and Le Bon Crubeen Café Bar and Restaurant. The restaurant was previously called The Talbot Lounge. There is entertainment seven nights a week.

_ _/_ _/20_ _

The Church Café Bar

Mary Street/Jervis Street, Dublin 1, (1) 828 0102
reservations@thechurch.ie, www.thechurch.ie

One of Dublin's most unusual pubs, located in the city centre's busiest shopping area, in what used to be a church, St Mary's. Arthur Guinness, founder of Guinness Brewery, married Olivia Whitmore here in 1761. It continued as a church until 1986 when it was turned into a retail outlet, then into a pub called W. J. M. Keating's, and finally into today's big tourist attraction, which comprises a café bar, restaurant and nightclub. The nightclub opens Fridays and Saturdays.

_ _/_ _/20_ _

J. & M. Cleary

36 Amiens Street, Dublin 1, (1) 855 2952

Opposite Connolly Station, under the railway bridge, this traditional local pub used to be known as The Signal House. There is another entrance in Foley Street which is open mainly on days when there are matches or other events on in Croke Park.

_ _/_ _/20_ _

Cill Airne

17 North Wall Quay, Dublin 1, (1) 952 4006
events@mvcillarne.com, www.mvcillairne.com

Commonly known as The Boat Bar and Restaurant, this is a highly atmospheric floating bar and restaurant. The *Cill Airne*, together with its sister ship, the *MV Blarna*, was commissioned by the Irish government in 1961, and built in the Liffey Dockyard in Dublin. The ship is moored near the O2 Complex and Samuel Beckett Bridge, and has great views of the River Liffey. Also on board is the Quay 16 Restaurant, Blue River Bar and Bistro, and The White Bar. A full history of this vessel is available on the Cill Airne's website.

_ _/_ _/20_ _

The Confession Box

88 Marlborough Street, Dublin 1, (1) 828 0028

At one time this traditional city centre pub was the smallest pub in Dublin, hence the name The Confession Box. Established in 1795 it was also previously called The Maid of Erin, F. O'Farrell's and A. McGill's. A light snack menu is served and there is regular entertainment.

_ _/_ _/20_ _

Cú Chulaínn's

69 Summerhill Parade, Summerhill, Dublin 1
Previously called The Barrel Inn, The Castle Inn, The Millennium and Whelan's, this traditional local pub dates back to 1908, as seen in the fascia on the building. It only opens for matches and events in Croke Park.

_ _/_ _/20_ _

Delahunty's

99 Upper Dorset Street, Dublin 1
(1) 830 4361
A traditional local house, established in 1946. It is sport-oriented with lots of great sporting pictures on the walls. There is regular entertainment.

_ _/_ _/20_ _

The Deer's Head (O'Reilly's)

151–152 Parnell Street, Dublin 1
(1) 874 0675
oreillys@live.ie
O'Reilly's The Deer's Head is a traditional local city centre pub, established in 1861. Its previous names were Galligan's, Judge's and Ryan's. Food is served every day and there is regular entertainment.

_ _/_ _/20_ _

Conway's

70 Parnell Street, Dublin 1
Scenes from the film *The Snapper* were shot in this city centre pub. The pub was established in 1745. It is currently closed.

_ _/_ _/20_ _

Dergvale Hotel Lounge

Dergvale Hotel, 4 Gardener Place, Dublin 1
(1) 874 4753
dergvale@indigo.ie
www.dergvalehotel.com
Hotel bar of the family-run Dergvale Hotel, once the home of Michael Cusack, co-founder of the GAA. It is an old-style lounge bar, mostly used by residents. and generally opens in the evenings.

_ _/_ _/20_ _

Dublin Supporters Bar

98 Parnell Street, Dublin 1
This bar's many previous names include Bermingham's, The Claddagh House, Murky Blues, The Sportsman, The Thorn Bush, Zogloba and most recently Starmusic. There is regular entertainment.

_ _/_ _/20_ _

Excise

Lower Mayor Street, Dublin 1
This establishment is currently trading as a restaurant. It is closed as a pub.

_ _/_ _/20_ _

Ely Bar and Brasserie

Stack A, Custom House Quay, IFSC, Dublin 1
(1) 672 0010
elybrasserie@elywinebar.com
www.elywinebar.com
Also known as Ely CHQ, this is a modern bar and bistro on the waterfront of George's Dock in the IFSC. It is housed in a former tobacco and wine warehouse which was built in the 1820s and boasts beautiful vaulted cellars. There is also an atrium bar and a heated waterside terrace. It has a large selection of wines. Ely have been trading in Dublin since 1999.

_ _/_ _/20_ _

Fibber Magee's

The Gate Hotel, 80 Parnell Street, Dublin 1
(1) 872 2575
manager@fibbermagees.ie
www.fibbermagees.ie
This bar and hard rock venue with regular live music is part of The Gate Hotel, which used to be O'Brien's Hotel. Previously called Bacchus, The Ivy Rooms, La Mirage, Slings Video Bar (the first video bar in Dublin) and Top Catz. It is a sister pub to Fibber's Rock Bar on Ormond Quay.

_ _/_ _/20_ _

The Findlater

80 Upper Dorset Street, Dublin 1
(1) 830 3750
A traditional local pub, previously called Conway's. There is regular entertainment.

_ _/_ _/20_ _

Floridita

Irish Life Centre, Abbey Street, Dublin 1
A bar and restaurant in the Irish Life Centre. It was previously called Life Bar. This establishment is currently closed.

_ _/_ _/20_ _

The Five Lamps (Humphrey's)

3 North Strand Road, Dublin 1
A traditional local pub known as Humphrey's Five Lamps. This establishment is currently closed.

_ _/_ _/20_ _

The Flowing Tide

9 Lower Abbey Street, Dublin 1, (1) 874 4108
A well-known traditional city centre pub patronised over the years by actors and patrons from the nearby Abbey Theatre. The pub was established in 1824, and was once called Dennis Hayes. A part of the bar in the basement is called The Neptune Lounge. The bar contains a stained glass window showing an image of 'King Neptune of the Deep'. A light snack menu is served and there is occasional entertainment.

_ _/_ _/20_ _

Gill's Corner House

Gill's Corner, 555 North Circular Road, Dublin 1
(1) 855 9224
This traditional local pub, established in 1920, is an historic landmark and is mentioned in many books on Dublin. It only opens part-time, usually on days when there are events on in Croke Park. There are many old match tickets and programmes on the walls of the back room and some old photos of Gill's, one of which bears the name 'Gill's The Park View House'.

_ _/_ _/20_ _

Gin Palace

42 Middle Abbey Street, Dublin 1
(1) 874 8881
ginpalace@fitzgeraldgroup.ie
www.louisfitzgerald.com
A Victorian-themed pub, established in 2003. The bar stocks over fifty different gins from around the world and serves food every day.

_ _/_ _/20_ _

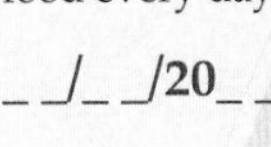

Glynn's The Wellington House

100 Upper Dorset Street, Dublin 1
Previously called The Meeting Pint, and also often called The Meeting Point, this traditional local pub traded as an off-licence in recent years, reopening as a pub in 2010. It contains some interesting bric-a-brac and pictures. A light snack menu is served and there is regular entertainment.

_ _/_ _/20_ _

The Good Bits

The Beresford Hotel, Store Street, Dublin 1
Part of the Beresford Hotel, this city centre bar and club opposite Busáras has two areas, one called The Cave and the other The Main Room. The pub was previously called The Isaac Butt Café Bar, Radio City Café Bar and The Cavern. This establishment is currently closed.

_ _/_ _/20_ _

Grainger's Corner

17 Amiens Street, Dublin 1
(1) 836 3249
A traditional city centre pub located opposite Connolly Station. It was established in 1928. Food is served every day and there is occasional entertainment.

_ _/_ _/20_ _

The Grand Central Café Bar

10–11 O'Connell Street, Dublin 1
(1) 872 8658
grandcentral@fitzgeraldgroup.ie
www.louisfitzgerald.com
A fine old 19th-century bank building, part of which was destroyed in the 1916 Rising. It was transformed into a bar in 2003, with lots of old safes and bank memorabilia. Food is served every day and there is occasional entertainment.

_ _/_ _/20_ _

The Grand Social

35 Lower Liffey Street, Dublin 1
(1) 874 0090
info@thegrandsocial.ie
www.thegrandsocial.ie
Located near the Ha'penny Bridge, this venue hosts live music, comedy, culture, DJs, art and performance. The bar hosts a flea market on Saturdays. It was previously called Pravda. There is entertainment most nights.

_ _/_ _/20_ _

The Green Room

Liffey Trust Centre, Sheriff Street, Dublin 1
(1) 894 4888
info@thegreenroombar.ie
www.thegreenroombar.ie
A modern bar near The O2 stadium complex, established in 2009. Home to the Red Room, which is a function room and an overflow bar when the main bar is busy, especially when music events are on in The O2 complex. On these nights the pub generally plays the performing group's music. Food is served every day and there is regular entertainment.

_ _/_ _/20_ _

Groome's Bar and Bistro

Cassidy's Hotel, Cavendish Row, Upper O'Connell Street, Dublin 1
(1) 878 0555
stay@cassidyshotel.com
www.cassidyshotel.com
Traditional bar and bistro of Cassidy's Hotel, just a stone's throw from O'Connell Street. 'A little gem in the heart of Dublin.' The hotel also houses Restaurant Six which is mainly used by residents.

_ _/_ _/20_ _

Harry's Bar

The O2 Centre, Point Village, Dublin 1
(1) 856 0733
harrysbar@pointvillage.ie
www.pointvillage.ie
This bar is open on event nights.

_ _/_ _/20_ _

The Harbourmaster Bar

Custom House Dock, Dublin 1
(1) 670 1688
info@harbourmaster.ie
www.harbourmaster.ie
This bar and restaurant was rebuilt from the shell of the old harbourmaster's office. It is situated alongside the waterfront of the Inner Dock, just off the River Liffey, and near the IFSC. Food is served every day.

_ _/_ _/20_ _

The Hemisemidemiquaver Bar

The Gibson Hotel, Point Village, Dublin 1
(1) 681 5000
info@thegibsonhotel.ie, www.thegibsonhotel.ie
The bar with the longest single word in its name of any pub in Dublin. Staff call it 'the Hemi Bar'. It is on the third floor of The Gibson Hotel, which opened in 2010 next to The O2 centre and The Point Luas station. The bar has a large heated terrace with great views of the city and the River Liffey. Food is served every day in the bar and in The Coda Eatery Restaurant.There are many pictures of famous musicians and bands throughout the hotel.

_ _/_ _/20_ _

The Hideout House

1 Campbells Row, Dublin 1
This is exactly what it says it is: a hideout, a traditional local pub hidden away just behind the Royal Canal, off Dorset Street, near Croke Park. It is always busy on match days and when events are on in Croke Park. It is one of the few establishments in Dublin where patrons play throw rings, where players throw rings onto a board like a darts board which has hooks with numbers. The pub was previously run by two sisters, Aggie and Molly Shannon.

_ _/_ _/20_ _

Hill 16

28 Middle Gardiner Street, Dublin 1
(1) 874 4239
tom@hill16pub.ie, www.hill16pub.ie
Named after a former standing area in Croke Park, this traditional local pub is always busy on match days and when events are held in Croke Park. It was established circa 1800. Food is served every day and there is regular entertainment.

_ _/_ _/20_ _

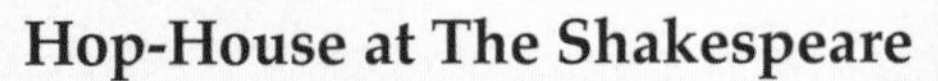

Hop-House at The Shakespeare

160 Parnell Street, Dublin 1
(1) 872 8318
www.hophouse.ie
Both a traditional Victorian city centre pub and home to The Kimchi Korean and Japanese restaurant. It is just off O'Connell Street.

_ _/_ _/20_ _

Hotel St George Bar

Hotel St George, 7 Parnell Square, Dublin 1
(1) 874 5611
info@hotel-st-george.ie
www.thecastlehotelgroup.com
This bar in 'Dublin's most elegant Georgian house hotel' is mostly used by hotel residents.

_ _/_ _/20_ _

Inntro Bar

Jury's Inn, Parnell Street, Dublin 1
(1) 878 4900
jurysinnparnellst@jurysinns.com
www.jurysinns.com
A hotel bar 'In the heart of it all'. The hotel also houses Infusion Restaurant and Il Barista Coffee. It is situated just off Parnell Square.

_ _/_ _/20_ _

Jack Nealon's

165 Capel Street, Dublin 1
(1) 872 3247
jacknealonspub@gmail.com
www.jacknealonspub.com
A traditional city centre pub, established in 1905. 'Modern contemporary meets old world charm.' There is a cocktail lounge upstairs. The pub's previous names were The Grattan, The Earl Grattan Rock Bar, The Kingsway Bar, Old Nuke's and Slattery's. A light snack menu is served.

_ _/_ _/20_ _

James Joyce Café Bar

Abbey Hotel, 52 Middle Abbey Street, Dublin 1
(1) 872 8188
reservations@abbey-hotel.ie
www.abbey-hotel.ie
This city centre hotel bar was previously called Bar 52 and Mojo's. Food is served every day and there is occasional entertainment.

_ _/_ _/20_ _

Joxer Daly's

103 Upper Dorset Street, Dublin 1
(1) 443 1976
The bar stools in this pub, which dates from 1818, are always occupied by great characters. The pub is painted in the Dublin and Kerry colours and has a rustic atmophere. It was previously called The Strand Bar. Its current name comes from Joxer Daly, a character in Seán O'Casey's play *Juno and the Paycock*. There is occasional entertainment.

_ _/_ _/20_ _

W. J. Kavanagh's of Dorset Street

4 Lower Dorset Street, Dublin 1
(01) 8730990
hello@wjkavanaghs.com
www.wjkavanaghs.com
Locally known as Little Kavanagh's—the name appears on a mosaic at the front door—this traditional pub has a large selection of craft beers. Food is served every day.

_ _/_ _/20_ _

Kavanagh's The Temple

71 Upper Dorset Street, Dublin 1
(1) 878 8308
info@templepub.com
www.templepub.com
Opened by Donal and Maureen Kavanagh in 1977, this traditional local pub and sports bar, with a strong GAA following, is now managed by their son, Dennis. Its previous names were Bannon's and Pat Sheary's. It is near Temple Street Children's Hospital. Food is served every day and there is regular entertainment.

_ _/_ _/20_ _

King 7 Bar and Restaurant

121 Capel Street, Dublin 1
(01) 8788988
A bar and restaurant in the city centre, serving both a bar menu and a Chinese menu. The venue has six private karaoke booths.

_ _/_ _/20_ _

The King's Inn

42 Bolton Street, Dublin 1
(1) 878 3895
A traditional local pub opposite King's College and DIT Bolton Street.

_ _/_ _/20_ _

Kudos

The Clarion Hotel, Excise Walk, North Wall Quay, Dublin 1
(1) 433 8800
kudos@clarionhotelifsc.com
www.clarionhotelifsc.com
Bar, lounge and restaurant of The Clarion Hotel in the IFSC. There is regular entertainment. The tall ship and famine museum, Jeanie Johnston, is moored in the nearby Custom House Quay, and can be seen from the hotel.

_ _/_ _/20_ _

Koh Restaurant and Cocktail Lounge

7 Jervis Street, Millennium Walkway, Dublin 1
(1) 814 6777
enquiries@koh.ie, www.koh.ie
A restaurant and cocktail lounge with a large bar that is well stocked with many spirits. The restaurant serves modern Thai and Asian cuisine.

_ _/_ _/20_ _

Knightsbridge Bar and Sinatra's Bar and Grill

The Arlington Hotel, 23–25 Bachelor's Walk, Dublin 1
(1) 804 9100
info@arlingtinhotel.ie
www.arlington.ie
The Knightsbridge Bar in The Arlington Hotel, which is around the corner from O'Connell Bridge, is furnished in a medieval style. Food is served every day and there is entertainment every night. The hotel is also home to Sinatra's Bar and Grill, and Cougars Nightclub (previously Boardwalk Club) which is open at weekends.

_ _/_ _/20_ _

Lagoona

Unit 4, Custom House Square, Dublin 1
(1) 791 8928
lagoonabarifsc@gmail.com
www.thesmithgroup.ie
A traditional-meets-modern bar established in 2003 in the centre of the IFSC. Food is served on weekdays.

_ _/_ _/20_ _

Lanigan's

The Clifton Court Hotel, 10–11 Eden Quay, Dublin 1
(1) 874 3535
info@cliftoncourthotel.ie laniganspub.cliftoncourthotel@gmail.com
www.cliftoncourthotel.ie
This hotel bar is also known as The Met Bar. The hotel was established in 1882 and was previously called Daly's. Food is served every day and there is regular entertainment.

_ _/_ _/20_ _

Le Monde Café Bar

The Beresford Hotel, 21 Store Street, Dublin 1
(1) 813 4700
info@beresfordhotelifsc.com
www.beresfordhotelifsc.com
Café bar of The Beresford Hotel, opposite Busáras and close to the IFSC. It is a great place to relax with a quiet drink. The hotel, which was previously called Hotel Isaacs, also houses Il Vignardo restaurant.

_ _/_ _/20_ _

The Living Room

Findlater Place, Cathal Brugha Street, Dublin 1
(1) 872 7169
murraypubgroup@gmail.com
A city-centre music bar just off O'Connell Street, a great place to watch sport. It has a beer garden with big-screen TVs. Food is served every day and there is regular entertainment.

_ _/_ _/20_ _

Lloyd's

46 Amiens Street, Dublin 1
(1) 855 5525
A traditional local pub on the edge of the city centre, established in 1893. A section of the pub bears the name Fitzpatrick's Bar. There is regular entertainment.

_ _/_ _/20_ _

Lowry's

16 Summerhill Parade, Dublin 1
A traditional local pub situated near Croke Park, offering regular entertainment. It was previously called Belton's and O'Neills.

_ _/_ _/20_ _

The Lotts Café Bar and The Lotts Snug

9 Lower Liffey Street, Dublin 1
(1) 872 7669
info@thelottscafebar.com
www.thelottscafebar.com
Established in 2004 this pub comprises a modern café bar and a snug bar: 'The Lotts Snug, Dublin's smallest bar' —a traditional bar showing sports on TV. Food is served every day and there is occasional entertainment.

_ _/_ _/20_ _

Madigan's of North Earl Street

25 North Earl Street, Dublin 1
(1) 874 6362
pubs@madigan.ie
www.madigan.ie
A renowned watering hole of literary greats including James Joyce, Brendan Behan and Patrick Kavanagh. It is near the statue of James Joyce. Part of the bar is called Joyce's Lounge. This traditional city centre pub, established in 1922, was the first pub in the Madigan chain. It boasts an original Harry Clarke stained glass feature. Food is served every day and there is regular entertainment.

_ _/_ _/20_ _

Madigan's of Abbey Street

4 Lower Abbey Street, Dublin 1
(1) 874 5456
pubs@madigan.ie
www.madigan.ie
A traditional city centre pub, serving food every day and with regular entertainment. It has traded as Madigan's since 1991.

_ _/_ _/20_ _

Madigan's of Connolly Station

Main Concourse, Connolly Station, Amiens Street, Dublin 1
(1) 611 7889
pubs@madigan.ie
www.madigan.ie
On the first floor of Connolly Station this traditional bar is a good place to relax while waiting for the train. Food is served during the week. Part of the bar is called The Bean and Gone Coffee Shop, a suitable name if you've just missed your train! The bar was previously called Oslo Bar.

_ _/_ _/20_ _

Madigan's of O'Connell Street

19 Upper O'Connell Street, Dublin 1
(1) 874 3692
pubs@madigan.ie
www.madigan.ie
Previously called The Nineteen O'Connell this traditional city centre pub was established in 1970 and has traded as Madigan's since 1984. Food is served every day and there is regular entertainment.

_ _/_ _/20_ _

Mayes

19a North Frederick Street, Dublin 1
(1) 874 6939
This traditional local pub situated just off Parnell Square was first licensed in 1812 and has traded as Mayes since 1989.

_ _/_ _/20_ _

McCoy's

The North Star Hotel, Amiens Street, Dublin 1
(1) 836 3136
reservations@northstarhotel.ie
www.northstarhotel.ie
A traditional hotel bar used by locals and guests. Food is served every day and there is regular entertainment. The hotel, which is situated opposite Connolly Station and near the IFSC, was established in the early 1900s.

_ _/_ _/20_ _

McNeill's

140 Capel Street, Dublin 1
(1) 874 7679
A small, cosy, well-furnished traditional pub with a good name for its Irish stew. It holds regular traditional Irish music sessions. The bar was J. McNeill's musical instrument shop from 1834 to 2008, and the music shop still trades, now on the first floor of the building.

_ _/_ _/20_ _

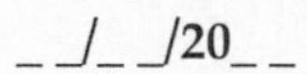

The Metro

155 Parnell Street, Dublin 1
(1) 874 0393
A traditional city centre early house situated just off O'Connell Street. The pub has traded as The Metro since 1957 and prior to that it was called Healy's and Murphy's. It was established in 1861.

_ _/_ _/20_ _

Molloy's

59 Talbot Street, Dublin 1
(1) 855 0017
An old traditional pub very much into sports and renowned for its great breakfasts. It was established circa 1866.

_ _/_ _/20_ _

Morley's

66 Summerhill Parade, Summerhill, Dublin 1
(1) 855 6617
A traditional local pub. It is currently only trading as an off-licence. The pub was previously called Cleary's.

_ _/_ _/20_ _

Mother Kelly's

74 Talbot Street, Dublin 1
(1) 817 0206
A traditional local pub, near Busáras and Connolly Station. Its previous names were Cheers Bon, Gallagher's, Lowry's and The Ramblers. Food is served every day and there is regular entertainment.

_ _/_ _/20_ _

Morrison Café Bar

The Morrison Hotel, Ormond Quay, Dublin 1
(1) 887 2400
bars@morrisonhotel.ie
www.morrisonhotel.ie
This boutique hotel was established in 1999. 'Probably the hippest and coolest luxury hotel in Dublin city centre.' It has a very relaxing candlelit lounge bar as well as a bar and café bar. The hotel also houses Halo Restaurant.

_ _/_ _/20_ _

The Moy

Upper Dorset Street, Dublin 1
A traditional local pub. This establishment is currently closed.

_ _/_ _/20_ _

Mullett's Pub

Amiens Street, Dublin 1
Dating back to the 1840s, this traditional local pub near Connolly Station traded as an off-licence in recent years. It reopened as a pub called Dooley's in 2011. It has now reverted to its previous name John Mullett's. The pub is mentioned in *Ulysses*, in which Bloom and Stephen go 'bevelling around by Mullett's'.

_ _/_ _/20_ _

Noctor's

34 Lower Sheriff Street, Dublin 1
(1) 855 7386
A traditional local pub tucked away behind Connolly Station and the IFSC.

_ _/_ _/20_ _

Ned Keenan's Bar

The Maple Hotel, 74–75 Lower Gardiner Street, Dublin 1
(1) 855 4271
info@mapelhotel.com
www.athelloguesthouse.com
Hotel bar of The Maple Hotel, which also incorporates the Othello Guest House. The hotel is five minutes' walk from Connolly Station. The bar has many pictures and quotes, some painted on the wall. One reads: 'TEENAGERS--tired of being harassed by your parents? ACT NOW!!! Move out, get a job, pay your bills… while you still know everything.' There is regular entertainment.

_ _/_ _/20_ _

Murray's Bar and Grill

33–34 Upper O'Connell Street, Dublin 1
(1) 878 7505
www.murraysbar.eu
A traditional city centre sports bar, previously called Frazer's and McGrath's. Before opening as a pub it was The Toro Bravo Restaurant. It was established circa 1988. Food is served every day and there is regular entertainment.

_ _/_ _/20_ _

The Oval

78 Middle Abbey Street, Dublin 1
(1) 872 1264
info@ovalpub.com
www.ovalpub.com
Named after The Oval cricket ground in London this traditional city centre pub is very much into sport. It was established in 1820 and is mentioned in James Joyce's *Ulysses*. I am told ladies were not served in this bar before 1960. Food is served every day.

_ _/_ _/20_ _

Oly's Bar and Restaurant

Jury's Inn, Custom House Quay, Dublin 1
(1) 854 1500
www.jurysinns.com
A bar and restaurant in Jury's Inn Custom House, in the IFSC. It was previously called Inntro Bar. The hotel opened in 1996.

_ _/_ _/20_ _

O'Mara's The Red Parrot

57 Dorset Street, Dublin 1
(1) 855 5053
A traditional local pub near Croke Park. It was previously called McGoldrick's. Food is served every day, and there is regular entertainment. My uncle Billy Moloney worked here in the 1950s.

_ _/_ _/20_ _

O'Shea's Hotel

O'Shea's Hotel, 19 Talbot Street, Dublin 1
(1) 836 5665
osheashotel@eircom.net
www.osheashotel.com
A traditional hotel bar, 'where a warm Irish welcome awaits you'. Food is served every day. There is music every night, including Irish dancing on Thursdays. Phil Lynott played here with The Black Eagles Band in the early days of his career, and Bono and The Edge played here with a band called The Hype in the 1970s before they formed U2. Bob Geldof and The Boomtown Rats also played here. The hotel is near Busáras and Connolly Station. It was previously called Moran's Hotel.

_ _/_ _/20_ _

PantiBar and Club

7–8 Capel Street, Dublin 1
(1) 874 0710
panti@ireland.com
www.pantibar.com
A gay venue, open every evening from 5pm. It is owned by the famous Dublin drag queen Miss Panti. It was previously called Gubu. There is entertainment most nights.

_ _/_ _/20_ _

Parnell Heritage Pub

72–74 Parnell Street, Dublin 1
(1) 987 6543
reservations@theparnell.com
www.theparnell.com
A pub has stood on this site opposite the Rotunda Hospital since around 1860. Previously called The Parnell Mooney, the pub had been closed for some years when it reopened as a gastro pub in 2012, keeping many of its original features. There are bars over three floors, including Captain Moonlight's Rooftop Bar and Grill on the upper level. Scenes from the film *The Snapper* were shot here. Many well-known Irish writers also drank here in the past, including Brendan Behan. There is occasional entertainment.

_ _/_ _/20_ _

The Pint

28 Eden Quay, Dublin 1
(1) 874 5255
www.thepint.ie
Sited along the quays beside Liberty Hall this traditional city centre pub and music venue was established in 1769. There are old memorial stones on the floor of this historic building. The pub was previously called Charlie P's and Soul 28. Food is served every day.

_ _/_ _/20_ _

The Plough

Lower Abbey Street, Dublin 1
Previously called The Firestone, Lanigan's Plough and The Plough, this traditional city-centre pub is situated opposite the Abbey Theatre. It is currently closed.

_ _/_ _/20_ _

Robert Reade

19 Store Street, Dublin 1
(1) 855 9992
A traditional city centre bar located beside the IFSC and Busáras. It was previously called Keating's. Food is served every day and there is occasional entertainment.

_ _/_ _/20_ _

Phil Ryan's The Hogan Stand

512 North Circular Road, Dublin 1
(1) 855 7838
A traditional local pub named after The Hogan Stand in nearby Croke Park. There is occasional entertainment.

_ _/_ _/20_ _

The Sackville

16 Sackville Place, Dublin 1
A traditional pub in the heart of the city just off O'Connell Street and opposite Clery's. A light snack menu is served every day.

_ _/_ _/20_ _

Saints and Scholars Bar

Wynn's Hotel, 35–39 Lower Abbey Street, Dublin 1
(1) 874 5131
info@wynnshotel.ie
www.wynnshotel.ie
A great old-style hotel lounge bar, traditionally used as a meeting place for country people in Dublin's city centre. Food is served every day. The hotel was established in 1845. It is also home to the Tomasso Ristorante.

_ _/_ _/20_ _

Saints and Sinners

North King Street, Dublin 1
A traditional local pub. This establishment is currently closed.

_ _/_ _/20_ _

Seán O'Casey's

105–106 Marlborough Street, Dublin 1
(1) 872 1665
Situated in the heart of Dublin, a few short steps from O'Connell Street, this real traditional pub is named after the famous Irish writer, Seán O'Casey, who once drank here. The bar is called O'Riordan's Bar. The pub was established circa 1900 and was previously called The High Tide. A light snack menu is served and there is regular entertainment.

_ _/_ _/20_ _

Sir Harry's Bar and Bistro

Academy Plaza Hotel, 1–14 Findlater Place, Dublin 1
(1) 878 0666
stay@academyplazahotel.ie
www.academyplazahotel.ie
This hotel bar was previously called Fadó Fadó. Food is served every day and there is entertainment. The hotel is near O'Connell Street. It also houses the Abacus restaurant.

_ _/_ _/20_ _

Sirens Bar

The Ormond Hotel, Ormond Quay, Dublin 1
A hotel bar situated in The Ormond Hotel. This establishment is currently closed.

_ _/_ _/20_ _

Slattery's

129 Capel Street, Dublin 1
(1) 874 6844
slatterysbar@gmail.com
www.slatterysbar.com
A traditional city centre pub and music venue, near Dublin City Council's fruit and vegetable market. It is an early house, and was once a famous music venue with many well-known names playing here in the past, including Phil Lynott, Shane McGowan and Christy Moore. The pub was established in 1842. Food is served every day.

_ _/_ _/20_ _

T. P. Smith's

9–10 Jervis Street / Abbey Street, Dublin 1
(1) 878 2067
info@thesmithgroup.ie
www.thesmithgroup.ie
A traditional city centre pub with an eye-catching copper spiral staircase, an impressive wall mosaic, and many other unique features. The pub has traded as T. P. Smith's since 2000. It was previously called Keating's, The Lady Gregory, and The Keg, and was relocated to a new premises down Jervis Street when the new Jervis Centre was built in 1996. Food is served every day.

_ _/_ _/20_ _

Stir Café Bar

The Maldron Hotel, Granby Row, Dublin 1
(1) 871 6888
info.parnellsquare@maldronhotels.com
www.maldronhotels.com
Café bar of The Maldron Hotel, which was previously called The Comfort Inn Dublin. Food is served every day.

_ _/_ _/20_ _

Stoney's Bar

Hill Street, Dublin 1
(1) 874 7919
A sign in this traditional local pub reads, 'May the roof above never fall in, and we friends below never fall out.' The pub was previously called Mulligan's. There is regular entertainment.

_ _/_ _/20_ _

The Strand House

172 North Strand Road, Dublin 1
A traditional local pub, previously called Grainger's. It closed in 2010 due to a fire, and reopened in 2011. There is regular entertainment.

_ _/_ _/20_ _

The Sunset House

1 Summerhill Parade, Summerhill, Dublin 1
A traditional local pub near Croke Park. It has occasional entertainment.

_ _/_ _/20_ _

Toddy's Bar and The Writers' Bar

The Gresham Hotel, 23 Upper O'Connell Street, Dublin 1, (1) 874 6881
info@thegresham.com, www.gresham-hotels.com
Toddy's Bar in The Gresham Hotel is named after the hotel's famous manager, Toddy O'Sullivan. Food is served in the bar every day. The hotel was established by Thomas Gresham in 1817, when O'Connell Street was called Sackville Street. It is home to the Gallery Restaurant and No. 23 Restaurant. The Writer's Bar is located in the hotel lobby.

_ _/_ _/20_ _

Trader John's Pub

Moore Street, Dublin 1
A traditional pub and early house situated on Moore Street Market. It is now trading as a betting shop.

_ _/_ _/20_ _

Ulysses Bar

The Ripley Court Hotel, 37 Talbot Street, Dublin 1
(1) 836 5892
sales@ripleycourthotel.com
www.ripleycourt.com
This hotel bar was previously called Austin Kelly's, The Dark Horse and The Theatre Bar. It is mainly used by residents. Food is served seven days a week. The hotel is situated close to Connolly Station.

_ _/_ _/20_ _

Vallence & McGrath's

81 North Wall Quay, Dublin 1
A traditional local pub. It was established in 1908, traded for 100 years, and is currently closed.

_ _/_ _/20_ _

The Vaults

Harbourmaster Place, IFSC, Dublin 1
(1) 605 4700
info@thevaults.ie
www.thevaults.ie
A bar, restaurant, multipurpose venue and nightclub established in 2002 in the IFSC, in ten interlinked vaults under Connolly Railway Station. They boast of having one of the best sound systems in Dublin. The venue is closed on Sundays.

_ _/_ _/20_ _

The Welcome Inn

93–94 Parnell Street, Dublin 1
Another traditional city centre pub 'where time stands still'. John, the proprietor, is a great historian of many Dublin pubs and helped me with my research. The pub was established in 1748. It is currently closed.

_ _/_ _/20_ _

The Waxie Dargle

6 Granby Row, Dublin 1
A traditional local pub situated just off Parnell Square. Its previous names were The Bodhrán, Europa, and The Granby.

_ _/_ _/20_ _

The Woolshed Sports Baa & Grill

Parnell Centre, Parnell Street, Dublin 1
(1) 872 4325
www.woolshedbaa.com
An Australian sports bar and grill, previously called The Outback. 'Dublin's best sporting bar'. There is a stepped seating area dedicated to watching sport on the big screen. Food is served every day and there is regular entertainment.

_ _/_ _/20_ _

The Bailey Limited
DUKE STREET DUBLIN 753181

3.9.51

To whom it may concern

I recommend very highly TOM O'MAHONY to all my colleagues.

Tom O'Mahony has been employed in the Bailey for more than 25 years.

He is a very skilled grill-cook with a very good caracter and spirit and is leaving the Bailey only for personal reasons.

Jean HADEY
Manager

DIRECTORS: ROGER GREENE (CHAIRMAN). KENNETH BESSON (MANAGING). J. VERLIN. P. J. McEVOY

My grandfather, Tommy O'Mahoney, worked in The Bailey as a chef for many years. This is the work reference he received upon leaving his job there. He actually met my grandmother, Polly Doyle, in this workplace, and when the management found out they were 'stepping out' together, she had to leave her employment. Some years later, when my mother was a teenager, they asked her to return to work there to fill a position that became vacant.

South City Centre

Dublin 2 comprises most of the south inner city.

The Bank of Ireland, College Green, housed the Irish Parliament in the late eighteenth century. It is an impressive building, and is situated opposite Trinity College Dublin.

Trinity College is Dublin's oldest university, founded in 1592 by Queen Elizabeth I. Trinity College library contains the famous Book of Kells, on public display together with an exhibition explaining its history.

Temple Bar is an area on the south side of the River Liffey, near the quays. It is considered Dublin's cultural quarter and has cobbled streets and a lively nightlife. It is especially popular with tourists.

Dublin Castle is located just off Dame Street, and was until 1922 the seat of British rule in Ireland. Now it is a major Irish government complex. The Castle, and the nearby Chester Beatty Library with its magnificent collection of Asian and Arab art, are popular tourist attractions.

Grafton Street is one of Dublin's two most-travelled shopping areas, the other being Henry Street. In recent years it was voted one of the world's most expensive shopping streets! Nonetheless, bargains can still be found here by the canny shopper.

St Stephen's Green, a public park located at the south end of Grafton Street, is the largest of the Georgian squares in Dublin. The park has many features including a lake, numerous statues, a bandstand, and fountains. There are musical performances in the bandstand throughout the summer (weather permitting).

The National Concert Hall, situated close to St Stephen's Green, is Ireland's principal venue for classical music concerts. As well as the main concert hall with its magnificent pipe organ, there are several smaller rooms used for chamber concerts and workshops.

The National Museum of Ireland Archaeology and History branch is sited on Kildare Street. Its exhibits include prehistoric, medieval and more recent Irish treasures.

The National Gallery of Ireland is situated opposite Merrion Square, another Georgian square and public park. The gallery houses the Irish national collection of Irish and European art.

The Natural History Museum (also part of the National Museum of Ireland) is situated close to the National Gallery, and is also opposite Merrion Square. Often called the Dead Zoo, it displays stuffed and mounted animals, as well as many animal skeletons. It is a museum piece in itself, as it has changed little since Victorian times.

Leinster House is home to the Oireachtas, the national parliament of Ireland. It consists of a complex of buildings situated between Merrion Square and Kildare Street. Built in the eighteenth century, it has since undergone many renovations and extensions.

Holles Street Hospital is also situated opposite Merrion Square. It is one of the three main maternity hospitals in Dublin.

The Bord Gais Energy Theatre is situated in the Docklands. It was completed in 2010 and is the largest theatre in Ireland.

37 Dawson Street Bar & Restaurant

37 Dawson Street, Dublin 2, (1) 902 2908
hello@37dawsonstreet.ie, www.37dawsonstreet.ie
Established in 2002, previously called Ron Black's Café Bar and Ron Black's Champagne Bar, and trading as 37 Dawson Street since 2012, this is a modern bar and restaurant with the theme 'all is not what it seems'. Also home to Ron's Whiskey Bar which stocks 37 different Irish whiskeys. On my first visit, I noticed many jars of loose sweets on the shelf behind the bar. The barman said they were complimentary and insisted I take a bag of bullseyes. Food is served every day and there is entertainment most nights.

_ _/_ _/20_ _

4 Dame Lane

4 Dame Lane, Dublin 2
(1) 679 0291
hello@4damelane.ie
www.4damelane.ie
Previously a snooker club, this bar opened as 4 Dame Lane in 1999. It is a modern bar, lounge and venue over two floors, with the Beat Suite club upstairs.

_ _/_ _/20_ _

Against The Grain

11 Wexford Street, Dublin 2, (1) 470 5100
www.winefoodbeer.com
A city centre bar with a large selection of beers. Food is served every day. 'Real food and global beers'. Previously called Carnival, Da-Two, Féile Café Bar and Nasdaq, it has traded as Against the Grain since 2010.

_ _/_ _/20_ _

Alfie's Bar and Grill

Conrad Hilton Hotel, Earlsfort Terrace, Dublin 2, (1) 602 8900
dublininfo@conradhotels.com, www.conraddublin.com
This is the bar of the Conrad Hilton Hotel, opposite the National Concert Hall, which opened in 1989. The bar is named after Dublin's much-loved mayor, Alfie Byrne (1882–1956). The hotel is also home to Alex Cocktail Bar and Restaurant. A girls' school, Alexandra College, used to be sited on Earlsfort Terrace. Food is served in the bar seven days a week.

_ _/_ _/20_ _

Amanda J's Bar and Restaurant

Travelodge Hotel, Lower Mercer Street, Dublin 2
(1) 478 0041
travelodge.ie, www.travelodge.ie
This hotel bar and restaurant, previously called Cusacks Bar and Restaurant, opened in 2012. It is housed within the Travelodge Hotel, previously Mercer's Hotel, which is located near Grafton Street. The building was previously Mercer's Hospital.

_ _/_ _/20_ _

Anseo

18 Lower Camden Street, Dublin 2
An old traditional city centre bar established in 1860, which describes itself as 'a vibrant and exciting music bar with cool sounds in comfy surroundings'. It has a large selection of world beers and spirits. There is music every night and comedy upstairs occasionally. Its previous names were Con's Pub, Corbetts, Meagher's and The Sword.

_ _/_ _/20_ _

The Auld Dubliner

24–25 Temple Bar, Dublin 2
(1) 677 0527
info@thesmithgroup.ie
www.thesmithgroup.ie
A lively traditional pub with constant live music and lots of craic. 'No such thing as strangers in The Dub, just auld friends who never met.' Those who know the pub refer to it as 'The Auld Dub'. Food is served every day.

_ _/_ _/20_ _

Aviator Lounge

Cliff Town House Hotel, 22 St Stephen's Green, Dublin 2
(1) 638 3939
info@theclifftownhouse.com
www.theclifftownhouse.com
This bar, on the first floor of The Cliff Townhouse Hotel, a luxury boutique hotel and restaurant, consists of two large connecting rooms with wonderful paintings throughout and model replica war planes suspended from the high ceiling.

_ _/_ _/20_ _

The Bailey

2–4 Duke Street, Dublin 2
(1) 670 4939
info@baileybarcafe.com
www.baileybarcafe.com
Established in 1834, many famous writers drank in this pub in the past. At one time the hall door of No. 7 Eccles Street, the home of Leopold and Molly Bloom of James Joyce's *Ulysses*, was hung in the interior. A plaque outside the pub explains this story. Over the years, the pub has changed into a modern trendy city centre pub. It serves food every day. My maternal grandfather, Thomas O'Mahoney, worked here.

_ _/_ _/20_ _

The Baggot Inn

143 Lower Baggot Street, Dublin 2
(1) 661 8758
reservations@thebaggotinn.ie
www.thebaggotinn.ie
A traditional city centre pub, formerly called T. Devine's, trading as the Baggot Inn since 1969. Once run by Jack Charlton, former Ireland football manager, it was known at that time as Big Jack's Baggot Inn. Many famous musicians have performed here, including U2, Christy Moore, Thin Lizzy, Mary Coughlan, The Waterboys, Brush Sheils, and Danny O'Donoghue of The Script. Food is served every day and there is regular entertainment.

_ _/_ _/20_ _

The Bank on College Green

20–22 College Green, Dublin 2
(1) 677 0677
info@bankoncollegegreen.com
www.bankoncollegegreen.com
A beautiful old bank building which was transformed into a great bar and restaurant in 2003. It retains many bank features, such as old safes. Food is served every day and there is regular entertainment. There is a facsimile of The Book of Kells just inside the main door.

_ _/_ _/20_ _

The Bankers

16 Trinity Street, Dublin 2
(1) 679 3697
thebankersbar@gmail.com
A traditional city centre pub previously called The Trinity Bar, also home to The Vault Lounge. It has regular entertainment and is renowned for its comedy nights. Food is served from Monday to Saturday.

_ _/_ _/20_ _

The Barge Inn

42 Charlemont Street, Dublin 2
(1) 475 1869
hickeygroupinfo@gmail.com
www.thebarge.ie
A traditional local bar beside the Grand Canal and Charlemont Bridge, established in 1799 and most recently refurbished in 1994. It was previously known as Jimmy Quinlan's. My uncle Billy Moloney served his time as a barman here in the 1950s. Food is served every day and there is regular entertainment.

_ _/_ _/20_ _

The Bernard Shaw

11–12 South Richmond Street, Portobello, Dublin 2
feeddack@bodytonicmusic.com
www.bodytonicmusic.com / thebernardshaw
A funky bar and music venue, also home to Bodytonic Club. It was previously called Bambrick's and Sonny Kine's Lotus Lounge. A pub was first established here in 1895. Food is served every day.

Becky Morgan's

9 Lower Grand Canal Street, Dublin 2
A traditional local pub, with regular entertainment. Food is served on weekdays.

_ _/_ _/20_ _

Bia Bar

The Drury Court Hotel, 30 Lower Stephen Street, Dublin 2, (1) 475 1988
reservations@drurycourthotel.ie, www.biabar.ie
Hotel bar of The Drury Court Hotel. 'Food, drink and dance in a cosmopolitan bar.' The bar was previously called Digger's Lane.

_ _/_ _/20_ _

The Bleeding Horse

24–25 Upper Camden Street, Dublin 2, (1) 475 2705
A traditional city pub established in 1649 and trading as The Bleeding Horse since 1710. Before then it was called The Falcon Inn. There are different stories about its current name. One tradition has it that in the 1600s wounded war horses were rounded up and doctored at the old pub on the site. Another tradition holds that when coach horses suffered from 'head staggers', they were bled here by a farrier. The pub is mentioned in James Joyce's *Ulysses*: 'I saw him in the Bleeding Horse a few times with Boylan the Billsticker.' Food is served every day and there is regular entertainment.

_ _/_ _/20_ _

The Blarney Inn

1–2 Nassau Street, Dublin 2
(1) 679 4388
info@kildarestreethoteldublin.com
www.kildarestreethoteldublin.com
Hotel bar of The Earl of Kildare Hotel which was founded as Elvidge's Family Hotel 'Serving Hospitality and Warming Hearts since 1837'. It is also home to Club Nassau 'home of the slow set'. The bar was previously called Harry's Bar. Food is served every day and there is regular entertainment, often including Irish dancing.

_ _/_ _/20_ _

The Bison Whiskey Bar

11 Wellington Quay,
Dublin 2
(1) 670 6692
info@theworkmansclub.com
www.theworkmansclub.com
A Wild-West themed pub, with saddle-shaped barstools, a range of paintings of the old American West on the walls and a bison's head mounted on the wall. A sign in the bar reads, 'Horse Parking Only: All Others Will be Towed'. The bar stocks 200 worldwide whiskies and 50 tequilas. It opened in 2012 and serves slow-roasted meats.

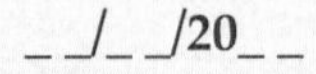

_ _/_ _/20_ _

Bowe's

31 Fleet Street, Dublin 2
(1) 671 4038
www.doylesintown.com
A traditional city centre pub, established in 1854, with a good atmosphere and lots of old-world charm. The pub stocks a large selection of whiskeys, and is described as 'Dublin's number 1 whiskey bar'. It serves a light snack menu and there is regular entertainment. I am told it was the first pub in Dublin to serve women.

_ _/_ _/20_ _

Break for The Border

The Grafton Capital Hotel, 2 Johnston's Place, Dublin 2
(1) 478 0300
info@breakfortheborder.com
www.breakfortheborder.com
Hotel bar and club of The Grafton Capital Hotel. Food is served every day in The Border Grill and there is regular entertainment.

_ _/_ _/20_ _

Brogan's

75 Dame Street, Dublin 2
A traditional city centre bar established in 1872 and decorated with Guinness memorabilia throughout the interior. It was previously called O'Brien's, Keerin's McCabe's, Leonard's, The Crampton Court, The City Hall Inn and The Viking Inn . The Viking was one of Dublin's earliest gay bars and has traded as Brogan's since the early 1990s.

_ _/_ _/20_ _

Bruxelles Café Bar and Lounges

7–8 Harry Street, Dublin 2
(1) 677 5362
info@bruxelles.ie
www.bruxelles.ie
A city centre sport and music bar, established in 1886. It was previously called The Grafton Mooney and The Zodiac Bar. The pub is divided into The Flanders Bar, The Saloon Bar and The New Zodiac Bar. Food is served every day and there is entertainment most nights.There is a statue of Phil Lynott of Thin Lizzy outside the pub .

_ _/_ _/20_ _

Buck Whaley's Café Bar and Nightclub

67 Lower Leeson Street, Dublin 2
(1) 633 4200
info@buckwhaleys.ie
www.buckwhaleys.ie
Also known as Buck's Townhouse this venue has four bars over two floors: The Piano Bar; The Terrace; The Master Room Nightclub, with state of the art LED dance-floor and sound system; and the VIP Boudoir Suite (members only). It opens most Thursdays and every weekend till late. It is named after Thomas "Buck" Whaley, an Irish politician and gambler who lived in Stephen's Green in the late 1700s.

_ _/_ _/20_ _

The Bull and Castle

5–7 Lord Edward Street, Dublin 2
(1) 475 1122
info@bullandcastle.ie
www.bullandcastle.ie
A gastro pub and venue, home to 'Ireland's only beer hall with over 150 world beers'. It also houses The FXB Steak and Seafood Restaurant and has regular entertainment. The pub was previously called The Castle Inn. A pub has traded here since around 1750, when the grandfather of the poet James Clarence Mangan ran a porter house here, possibly one of the first Dublin pubs to serve Guinness.

_ _/_ _/20_ _

Buswell's Bar

Buswell's Hotel, 23–27 Molesworth Street, Dublin 2
(1) 614 6500
buswells@quinn-hotels.com
www.quinnhotels.com
Buswell's Hotel bar is often frequented by politicians due to its convenient location opposite Dáil Éireann. Food is served every day. The hotel was established in 1882. It is also home to Truman's Restaurant.

_ _/_ _/20_ _

Buskers' Bar and The Rendezvous Bar

Temple Bar Hotel, Fleet Street, Dublin 2, (1) 677 3333
reservations@tbh.ie buskers@tbh.ie alchemy@tbh.ie
www.templebarhotel.com www.buskersbar.com www.alchemyclub.ie
Busker's is a trendy disco bar in The Temple Bar Hotel. DJs play late most nights and it attracts a young crowd. The hotel also houses Alchemy Nightclub, previously called Boomerang and Sloopies which opens mainly at weekends. The Rendezvous Bar is a traditional residents' bar in the hotel. The hotel is also home to the Terrace Grill Restaurant.

_ _/_ _/20_ _

C Central Bar Lounge and Bistro

The Camden Court Hotel, Upper Camden Street, Dublin 2
(1) 475 9666
sales@camdencourthotel.com
www.camdencourthotel.com
Hotel bar of The Camden Court Hotel, previously called Piseógs. It serves food every day. The hotel is also home to the Iveagh Restaurant.

_ _/_ _/20_ _

Café Cairo Bar

Trinity Capital Hotel, Pearse Street, Dublin 2
(1) 648 1000
info@trinitycapitalhotel.com
www.trinitycapitalhotel.com
Hotel bar of The Trinity Capital Hotel. The bar and lobby are decorated with Egyptian-themed furnishings. Food is served every day.

_ _/_ _/20_ _

Café en Seine

39–40 Dawson Street, Dublin 2, (1) 677 4567
info@cafeenseine.ie, www.cafeenseine.ie
A spectacular French-style café bar established in 1993, with the Wow! factor turned on from the moment you walk through the door into the extensive 19th-century Parisian-style interior. At the back of the building is a three-storey atrium in which there are many tall trees, glass-panelled ceilings, enormous Art Nouveau-style glass lanterns and statues. This establishment is one of Dublin's top attractions for food, drink and late night entertainment.

_ _/_ _/20_ _

The Camden Palace Bar and Nightclub

84–87 Lower Camden Street, Dublin 2
(1) 478 0808
info@thecamdenpalace.com
www.thecamdenpalace.com
A venue and hotel bar of the Camden De Luxe Hotel, previously the Camden De Luxe Theatre and Cinema, often referred to by its previous name, Planet Murphy. The bar has American pool tables. The space upstairs used to be a snooker room, and is now 'Dublin's hottest nightclub', opening Thursdays, Fridays and Saturdays. Scenes from the film *The Commitments* were shot here. Bar food is served on weekdays.

_ _/_ _/20_ _

The Capitol Lounge

1 Aungier Street, Dublin 2
(1) 475 7166
info@capitol.ie
www.capitol.ie

A trendy bar and cocktail lounge which opens late every night. It attracts a young crowd.

_ _/_ _/20_ _

Captain America's

The Irish Writers' Co-operative, which signalled a new era in Irish literature and publishing, was born at a meeting here in Captain Americas in 1975.

44 Grafton Street, Dublin 2
(1) 671 5266
dublin@captainamericas.com
www.captainamericas.com

The first Captain America's in Dublin, established in 1971, this is a bar, restaurant and music venue. There are two plaques at the entrance: one pays tribute to the Irish Writers Co-operative which was set up here, and the other is a Rock 'N' Stroll Trail plaque dedicated to Chris de Burgh who played in the bar at an early stage of his career. The restaurant has a collection of music memorabilia, and is decorated with original murals by Irish artist Jim Fitzpatrick. There is regular entertainment in the Captain's Live Bar.

_ _/_ _/20_ _

Carlisle Café Bar

O'Connell Bridge House, Burgh Quay, Dublin 2
(1) 677 7409
qbardublin@gmail.com
www.quinnhotels.com

A café bar and a nightclub called the Q Bar and Club situated near O'Connell Bridge, which used to be called the Carlisle Bridge. This pub was previously called The Harp Bar. Food is served every day and there is entertainment most nights.

_ _/_ _/20_ _

Cassidy's Pub

42 Lower Camden Street, Dublin 2
(1) 475 6540

A traditional local city centre Victorian pub, established in 1856, previously called Caulfield's and Delahunty's. It has traded as Cassidy's since 1968. Many famous writers have frequented this pub over the years, and President Bill Clinton visited here on 1st December 1995 and again on 13th May 2005. Lunch is served on weekdays.

_ _/_ _/20_ _

Cassidy's Bar

27 Westmoreland Street, Dublin 2
A bar and live music venue near O'Connell Bridge, established in 1856. It was previously called The Westmoreland. This pub was once the home of the *Freeman's Journal*, the oldest nationalist newspaper in Ireland. Food is served every day and there is entertainment most nights.

_ _/_ _/20_ _

Chaplin's

1–2 Hawkins Street, Dublin 2
(1) 677 5225
A city centre pub very much into sport, and with regular entertainment. The pub was previously called O'Reilly's and The Regal Inn. It serves a light snack menu.

_ _/_ _/20_ _

The Cellar Bar and No 23 Bar

The Merrion Hotel, Upper Merrion Street, Dublin 2
(1) 603 0600
info@merrionhotel.com
www.merrionhotel.com
The Cellar Bar and Restaurant is sited in the original 18th-century wine vaults of The Merrion Hotel, with bare brick walls and vaulted ceilings. The hotel is opposite Government Buildings and houses Restaurant Patrick Guilbaud. The No 23 Bar serves cocktails and canapes in a luxurious setting.

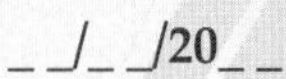
_ _/_ _/20_ _

The Chocolate Bar

Harcourt Street, Dublin 2
A collection of music venues and clubs, The Chocolate Bar, Crawdaddy, The Pod and The Tripod, were housed in what was once Harcourt Street Railway Station. This establishment is currently closed.

_ _/_ _/20_ _

Clarendon Café Bar

32 Clarendon Street, Dublin 2
(1) 617 0060
www.theclarendonbar.com
A three-floored city centre bar just off Grafton Street. The top floor is called The Penthouse Bar. It was previously called Champer's. Food is served every day and there is regular entertainment.

_ _/_ _/20_ _

Copper Face Jacks

The Jackson Court Hotel, 29–30 Harcourt Street, Dublin 2
(1) 475 8777
info@jackson-court.ie
www.jackson-court.ie
Bar and nightclub of The Jackson Court Hotel. Lunch is served on weekdays in the bar. The nightclub opens every night and is a well-known meeting place for gardaí, nurses and teachers.

_ _/_ _/20_ _

The Czech Inn

Essex Gate, Dublin 2
(1) 671 1535
www.czech-inn.org
Previously known as Isolde's Tower, this pub in the centre of Temple Bar has been trading as The Czech Inn since 2006 and is now a Czech-themed gastro pub, with 100 different types of beer available. It is also home to Club C. There is entertainments most nights.

_ _/_ _/20_ _

D | two Bar and Club

The Harcourt Hotel, 60 Harcourt Street, Dublin 2
(1) 478 3677
info@dtwonightclub.com
www.dtwonightclub.com
Bar and club of The Harcourt Hotel, previously known as The Harcourt Inn. Food is served every day and there is regular entertainment. The hotel also has a large garden with a bar where barbeques are held on summer evenings. The hotel residents' bar is called Barney Googles. The restaurant is called Little Caesar's. Part of this building was once the home of Irish playwright George Bernard Shaw.

_ _/_ _/20_ _

Dakota

9 South William Street, Dublin 2, (1) 672 7696
info@dakotabar.ie, www.dakotabar.ie
A large modern city centre bar established in 2000. It comprises a single large room, which was formerly a fabric warehouse for a nearby department store. Food is served every day.

_ _/_ _/20_ _

The Dame Tavern

18 Dame Court, Dublin 2
A city centre traditional house, established around 1890, with music sessions most nights. It is a place where many characters congregate. The pub is often referred to as The Stag's Tail; it was previously called The Van Gogh. The painting by Daithi Brophy reproduced here hangs in the bar and shows some of the pub's regular patrons enjoying a drink.

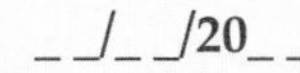

_ _/_ _/20_ _

Dandelion Boutique Café Bar and Club

2 St Stephen's Green West, Dublin 2, (1) 476 0870
info@welovedandelion.com, www.welovedandelion.com
A café bar and club, on the site of the old Dandelion Market, big on sport with five bars and entertainment most nights. Food is served every day. At one time this was home to a branch of the Planet Hollywood bar and restaurant chain. The plaque records that U2 played in the old Dandelion Market in their early days.

_ _/_ _/20_ _

The Dark Horse Inn

1 Burgh Quay, Dublin 2
(1) 675 1862
darkhorseinn@gmail.com
A modern lounge bar and one of Dublin's early houses, established around 1790. It was previously known as McCormack's of Burgh Quay and The White Horse Inn. Food is served Monday to Saturday and there is regular entertainment.

_ _/_ _/20_ _

Darkey Kelly's

Harding's Hotel, Copper Alley, Temple Bar, Dublin 2
(1) 679 6500
info@hardinghotel.ie
www.hardinghotel.ie
A traditional local pub in Harding's Hotel. It serves food every day and there is regular entertainment. The hotel also houses the Copper Alley Bistro. Previously dubbed the 'Maide' Tower, in the 18th century this building was a brothel run by Madam Darkey Kelly, who was publicly executed in 1740 for the alleged murder of her child. Copper Alley is one of Dublin's oldest medieval streets.

_ _/_ _/20_ _

Davy Byrne's

21 Duke Street, Dublin 2
(1) 677 5217
www.davybyrnes.com
A traditional city centre house and gastro pub, established in 1889. Their signature dish is Irish stew, and they also serve great seafood. Davy Byrne's featured in James Joyce's *Ulysses*, where it was called a 'moral pub'.

_ _/_ _/20_ _

The Dawson Lounge

25 Dawson Street, Dublin 2
(1) 671 0311
Dublin's smallest pub, previously called Ron Black's. It is approximately 350 square feet in size. Most nights there are about twenty people in and around the bar. However, there is always room for one more! You enter by a spiral staircase down to the basement. 'An intimate and friendly pub.' A light snack menu is served every day.

_ _/_ _/20_ _

Delaney's

18 Aungier Street, Dublin 2
(1) 475 3808
A traditional city centre local pub, offering regular entertainment. It was previously called The Central Bar, Delaney's and Gleesons.

_ _/_ _/20_ _

Devitt's The Cusack Stand

78 Lower Camden Street, Dublin 2
(1) 475 3414
devittspub@gmail.com
A family-run traditional city centre pub, previously called Ahearn's. It has a great emphasis on sport and music, with many GAA sporting pictures in the bar. The lounge upstairs, An Poc Fada, has regular live music (usually sessions). Lunch is served on weekdays.

_ _/_ _/20_ _

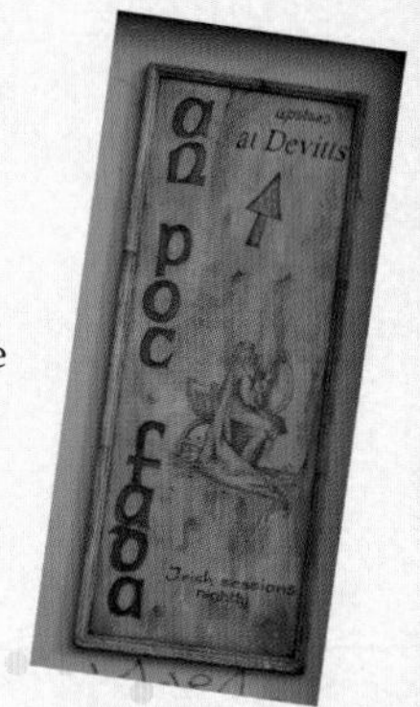

DICEYS
GARDEN

Dicey's Garden Bar

The Russell Court Hotel, 21–25 Harcourt Street, Dublin 2
(1) 478 4066
events@russellcourthotel.ie info@krystlenightclub.com
www.russellcourthotel.ie www.krystkenightclub.com
A bar and two nightclubs are situated in The Russell Court Hotel. Dicey's Garden Bar, previously called Dicey Reilly's, has an award-winning beer garden and holds summer barbeques. It serves food on weekdays and has regular entertainment. Bojos 35, previously called Bojangles, is aimed at parygoers over 30 and plays chiefly '60s, '70s and '80s music. Krystle Nightclub has two large bars and a heated beer garden. 'Dublin's Elegant Alternative'. The clubs open Friday and Saturday nights.

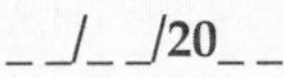
_ _/_ _/20_ _

Doheny & Nesbitt's

5 Lower Baggot Street, Dublin 2
(1) 676 2945
A Dublin landmark pub, established in 1867, 'where time has stood still, where every stranger is a friend and where drinking is almost an art form and where knowledge is learned and where history takes place'. The pub is named after previous owners Ned Doheny and Tom Nesbitt. It is well known as a gathering place for Dublin's newspaper journalists. Food is served from Monday to Saturday.

_ _/_ _/20_ _

Doolan's

45 Hogan Place, Dublin 2
A traditional local pub, previously called Biddy's and Lynch's. A good place for watching sport, it also has regular entertainment.

_ _/_ _/20_ _

Doyles in Town

8–9 College Street, Dublin 2
(1) 671 0616
bookings@doylesintown.com
www.doylesintown.com
Established in 1880 and run by the Doyle family since 1977, this pub's previous names were The College Mooney, The College Inn, The Fleet and The Oscar Wilde. Hostel / guesthouse accommodation, called 'The Times We Live In' is also provided. Its reception area was previously an off-licence called O'Donohoe's.

_ _/_ _/20_ _

The Dragon

65 South Great George's Street, Dublin 2
(1) 478 1590
A vibrant gay bar and nightclub, offering regular entertainment. It was previously called SoSuMe and has traded as The Dragon since 2005, the name a playful tribute to The George pub up the road, Dublin's oldest-established gay pub.

_ _/_ _/20_ _

The Duke

8–9 Duke Street, Dublin 2
(1) 679 9553
A traditional city centre pub established in 1882 and named after the 2nd Duke of Grafton, and previously called Tobin's. Many famous Irish writers used to drink here in the past, and the pub is a starting point for the Dublin Literary Pub Crawl. There is a Rock 'N' Stroll Trail plaque on the front of the pub to The Hothouse Flowers. Food is served every day and there is regular entertainment.

Rock 'N' Stroll Trail
Hothouse Flowers

_ _/_ _/20_ _

Eamonn Doran's Tavern on the Green

104–105 Lower Leeson Street, Dublin 2
(1) 661 8603
eamonndorantotg@gmail.com
This bar opened as Eamonn Doran's in 2011. Many famous Irish writers used to drink here when the pub was known as Alfie Mulligan's on the Green or O'Dwyer's. I am told there used to be a pot belly stove in the pub on which staff used to cook. Apparently this created a really smokey atmosphere! Lunch is served every day and there is regular entertainment.

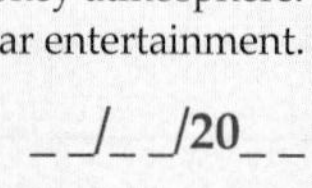

_ _/_ _/20_ _

Ely Gastro Pub

Forbes Street, Hanover Building, Hanover Quay, Dublin 2
(1) 633 9986
elygastropub@elywinebar.com
www.elywinebar.com
Also known as Ely HQ, this large gastro pub is situated on the waterfront of the Grand Canal Dock and opposite the Bord Gáis Energy Theatre. Ely have been trading in Dublin since 1999.

_ _/_ _/20_ _

The Exchequer Bar Gastro Pub

3–5 Exchequer Street, Dublin 2
(1) 670 6787
info@theexchequer.ie
www.theexchequer.ie
A gastro pub attached to The Central Hotel that opened in 2009. It has had many previous names but the one I remember is Rainbow's. Most recently it was called Ross and Walpole (the names of the men who built the hotel in 1887) and La Vie. There is regular entertainment.

_ _/_ _/20_ _

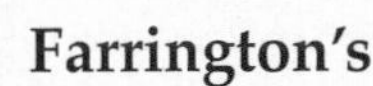

Farrington's

28–29 East Essex St, Dublin 2
(1) 671 5135
farringtonsoftemplebar@eircom.net
www.thesmithgroup.ie
A very old pub, established in 1696 in the centre of Temple Bar, previously called J. J. O'Neill's, The Norseman and Timmon's. It also provides accommodation and serves food every day. There is entertainment most nights.

_ _/_ _/20_ _

The Ferryman (O'Brien's)

35 Sir John Rogerson's Quay, Dublin 2
(1) 671 7053
reservation@ferrymanhotel.com
www.theferrymanhotel.com
O'Brien's The Ferryman is a traditional local pub and hotel situated next to the Samuel Beckett Bridge. The hotel was established in 1780. Food is served every day and there is regular entertainment.

_ _/_ _/20_ _

Fitzgerald's

22 Aston Quay, Dublin 2
(1) 677 9289
info@fitzgeraldsbar.ie
www.fitzgeraldsbar.ie
A traditional city centre pub located next to O'Connell Bridge. It was previously called The Daniel O'Connell Lounge and O'Mara's. It has probably the smallest smoking area in Dublin. Food is served every day and there is regular entertainment.

_ _/_ _/20_ _

Flannery's Bar and Café

6 Lower Camden Street, Dublin 2
(1) 478 2238
Established in 1839 this traditional city centre pub used to be called The Camden House and O'Toole's. There is entertainment most nights but in spite of the name food is not served.

_ _/_ _/20_ _

Fitzsimon's Temple Bar

Eustace Street, Dublin 2
(1) 677 9315
info@fitzsimonshotel.com
www.fitzsimonshotel.com
Fitzsimons' boutique hotel and nightclub near the Millennium footbridge, has bars spread over various floors, including one with an open-air roof terrace. Food is served every day and there is entertainment every night.

_ _/_ _/20_ _

The Foggy Dew

1 Fownes Street and Crow Street, Dublin 2
(1) 677 9328
www.thefoggydew.ie
A traditional city centre pub next to the Central Bank, established in 1901 and previously called Moran's. The pub has a rock music theme with framed golden discs on the walls and two signed electric guitars behind the bar. Food is served on weekdays and there is regular entertainment.

_ _/_ _/20_ _

Foley's

1 Merrion Row, Dublin 2
(1) 661 0115
info@foleysbar.com
www.foleysbar.ie
A traditional local pub in the heart of the city, which has traded as Foley's since 1979. Part of the pub was formerly Reilly's chemist shop and this was extended into Foley's some years ago. Food is served daily in the bar and in Queen Maedhbh's restaurant upstairs. There is traditional music most nights.

_ _/_ _/20_ _

The Front Lounge

33–34 Parliament Street, Dublin 2
(1) 670 4112
info@thefrontlounge.ie
www.thefrontlounge.ie
A city centre music bar that opened in the 1990s. With its relaxed, comfortable atmosphere, it attracts both a gay and straight crowd and is known as a gay-friendly pub. It serves food on weekdays and has regular entertainment. There is a second entrance in Exchange Street, with a sign over the door saying 'The Back Lounge'. A pub called The Red Hackle was once on or near this site.

_ _/_ _/20_ _

The Garage Bar

East Essex Street, Dublin 2
(1) 679 6543
thegaragebartemplebar@gmail
A casual modern pub that looks like an old garage, with an old petrol pump and the front end of a Mini car mounted to a wall. Old wooden cable reels serve as tables and seating and there is sawdust on the floor. Before closing for a long time, old bus seats were used for some of the customer seating. Garage reopened in 2010. There is entertainment most nights.

_ _/_ _/20_ _

The George Bar and Club

12–13 South Great George's Street, Dublin 2
(1) 671 3819
info@thegeorge.ie
www.thegeorge.ie
Founded in 1985, this bar is a venerable institution for Dublin's gay community. It is the oldest and best-known gay bar in Dublin, with entertainment most nights. It is renowned for its Sunday night bingo hosted by TV personality Shirley Temple Bar, aka Declan Buckley.

_ _/_ _/20_ _

The Ginger Man

40 Fenian Street, Dublin 2
(1) 676 6388
gingermand2@gmail.com

A traditional local pub located near Trinity College, previously called The Merry Inn; up to 1947, it was called Hayes. It is now named after the novel *The Ginger Man* by J. P. Donleavy. Food is served every day.

_ _/_ _/20_ _

Gogarty's Vat House

Bloom's Hotel, 6 Anglesea Street, Dublin 2
(1) 671 5622
vathouse@blooms.ie events@clubm.ie
www.vathouse.ie www.clubm.ie
This traditional Irish bar in Bloom's Hotel was built from old timbers taken from the Guinness Brewery at St James's Gate. Food is served every day and there is entertainment every night. The hotel is also home to Club M nightclub.

_ _/_ _/20_ _

The Globe Bar

11 South Great Georges Street, Dublin 2
(1) 671 1220
info@globe.ie
www.globe.ie
A city centre bar, club—the Rí Rá—and venue, with entertainment most nights.

_ _/_ _/20_ _

The Grafton Lounge

Unit 2, Royal Hibernian Way / Duke Lane, Dublin 2
(1) 679 6260
reservations@thegraftonlounge.ie
www.thegraftonlounge.ie
A modern bar and club. Situated just off Grafton Street, it was formerly owned by Eddie Irvine under the name of Cocoon and was more recently called Noo Bar. Food is served every day and there is regular entertainment.

__/__/20__

The Green Room Bar

The Pearse Hotel, 98–107 Pearse Street, Dublin 2
(1) 670 3666
info@pearsehotel.com
www.pearsehotel.com
Hotel bar of The Pearse Hotel, previously The Holiday Inn. Food is served in the bar every day and the hotel is also home to The Pearse Brasserie.

__/__/20__

Grogan's Castle Lounge

15 South William Street, Dublin 2
(1) 677 9320
www.groganspub.ie
A traditional city centre pub established in 1899. It holds a continually changing art exhibition, and is famous for being a host to Dublin writers. Sandwiches are served.

__/__/20__

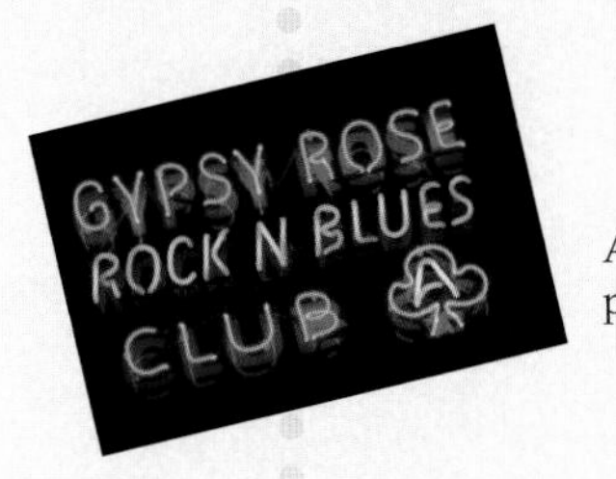

Gypsy Rose

5 Aston Quay, Dublin 2
(1) 672 5566
www.gypsyroseclub.com
A rock 'n' blues bar that opened in 2010. It was previously called The Viper Room Theatre Bar, a late bar whose slogan was 'Nobody's ugly after 2 a.m.'.

__/__/20__

The Hairy Lemon

42 Lower Stephen Street, Dublin 2
(1) 671 8949
www.thehairylemon.ie
A traditional old-world city centre pub, previously known as The Pygmalion and The William Tell, with lots of bric-a-brac on every wall and hanging from the ceiling. It is named after a famous local Dublin character with a lemon-shaped face. It has many nooks and crannies and there is always a good atmosphere here. Food is served in the Lemon Cafe every day.

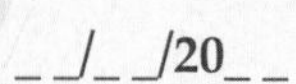

_ _/_ _/20_ _

Handel's

George Frederic Handel Hotel, 16–18 Fishamble Street, Christchurch, Dublin 2
(1) 6709404
info@georgefrederichandelhotel.com
www.georgefrederichandelhotel.com
This bar in The George Frederic Handel Hotel was previously called Handel's Bar and Karma. Food is served every day.

_ _/_ _/20_ _

The Ha'penny Bridge Inn

42 Wellington Quay, Dublin 2
(1) 677 0616
A traditional city centre pub, with a comedy venue called The Battle of the Axes. It is next to the Ha'penny Bridge, one of Dublin's first pedestrian toll bridges which was built in 1816. It was officially named the Iron Bridge, but because people were charged a halfpenny to cross the bridge, it became commonly known as the Ha'penny Bridge. The toll charge was dropped in 1919. The name in Irish as seen on the pub sign is *Leath Phingin* Inn. The pub was previously called Jim Moran's and I was told by the current owner, Mick Ryan, that at one time it was owned by Josef Locke, the renowned Irish tenor. A light snack menu is served every day and there is regular entertainment.

_ _/_ _/20_ _

Hard Rock Café

Fleet Street, Temple Bar, Dublin 2
(1) 671 7777
sales@hardrockcafe.ie
www.hardrockcafe.com
A branch of the globally-known bar / restaurant chain. Its Rock 'N' Roll Restaurant and Rock Shop sells hard rock merchandise. There are many signed guitars and rock memorabilia throughout the restaurant. It was previously called The All Sports Bar.

_ _/_ _/20_ _

Harry's on the Green

South King Street, Dublin 2
(1) 475 8504
info@harrysonthegreen.ie
www.harrysonthegreen.ie
A comfortable modern Manhattan-style cocktail bar which opened in 2010. The bar was previously called Down Under, Major Tom's, Ruaille Buaille and The Scene. They have an original-style Bacardi Bar. Food is served every day and there is regular entertainment.

_ _/_ _/20_ _

Hartigan's

100 Lower Leeson Street, Dublin 2
(1) 676 2280
A traditional local pub located just off St Stephen's Green. It is known as John Hartigan's and is locally called John's. The pub was previously called Thomas John Lynch's. The initial letters of this title (TJL) are still displayed on the stained glass windows at the front of the pub.

_ _/_ _/20_ _

Hogan's

36 South Great George's Street, Dublin 2
(1) 677 5904
A traditional-meets-modern pub, housed within Kelly's Hotel, Dublin. It offers regular entertainment. Hogan's was once known as The Hogan Stand and still bears a sign with this name outside. It was established in 1878.

_ _/_ _/20_ _

The Horseshoe Bar and The No 27 Bar

The Shelbourne Hotel, 27 Stephen's Green, Dublin 2
(1) 663 4500
reservations@renaissancehotels.com
www.marriott.com
These bars are in The Shelbourne Renaissance Hotel, which is part of the Marriott hotel group and one of Dublin's most elegant buildings. The hotel, which was first established in 1824, was refurbished to a high standard in 2008. It is also home to The Saddle Room Restaurant.

_ _/_ _/20_ _

Hourican's

7 Lower Leeson Street, St Stephen's Green, Dublin 2
(1) 678 9030
www.houricans.com
A traditional local old world pub with lots of pictures and old road signs throughout. The pub was established around 1930 and has traded as Hourican's since 1978. It serves food every day.

_ _/_ _/20_ _

The IFI Bar

Irish Film Institute, 6 Eustace Street,
Temple Bar, Dublin 2
(1) 679 5744
info@irishfilm.ie
www.ifi.ie
A cosy modern bar situated within The Irish Film Institute which has two cinemas. Food is served every day.

Howl At The Moon

7 Lower Mount Street, Dublin 2
(1) 634 5460
info@howlatthemoon.ie
www.howlatthemoon.ie
A bar and club with four bars on four levels, which include The Zimmer Room, The Hoity Toity Bar, and a roof terrace, currently open at weekends. It was previously called O'Dwyer's and was once a famous music venue. A pub has stood on or near this site since 1817.

_ _/_ _/20_ _

The Inn On The Green

The Fitzwilliam Hotel, 2 St Stephen's Green, Dublin 2
(1) 478 7000
enq@fitzwilliamhotel.com
www.fitzwilliamhotel.com
A traditional hotel bar in The Fitzwilliam Hotel which also houses Thornton's Restaurant and The Citron Restaurant. Food is served in the bar every day.

_ _/_ _/20_ _

The International Bar and Lounge

23 Wicklow Street, Dublin 2
(1) 677 9250
www.international-bar.com
Established in 1780 this traditional pub has been run by the Donohoe family since circa 1888. The pub gained its name from the flags of various nations which used to be on display. There is entertainment in the bar most nights, which often includes impromptu music sessions. The Duke Box Bar in the basement and the Comedy Lounge upstairs both open every night. Many famous Irish writers drank here. A light snack menu is available in the bar every day.

_ _/_ _/20_ _

Izakaya Bar

12–13 South Great George's Street, Dublin 2
(1) 645 8001
www.yamamori.ie
A Japanese sake bar on the lower ground floor of The Yamamori Oriental Café. It is run by the Ryan family who are very enthusiastic about Asian culture. The historic building, which was previously home to one of Bewley's first cafés, retains many of its original features. The bar has a good selection of world beers, including Nipponia Draught Beer from Japan. The Ryans tell me it is the only place in Europe selling this particular beer. Yamamori restaurants have been established in Dublin since 1995, and the Yamamori Oriental Café opened in 2011. There is regular entertainment in the bar.

_ _/_ _/20_ _

Jasmine Bar

Brook's Hotel, 59 Drury Street, Dublin 2
(1) 670 4000
reservations@brookshotel.ie
www.brookshotel.ie
This bar in Brook's Hotel was previously called The Butter Lane Bar. It has a large selection of whiskeys of the world (approximately 120 bottles), which they call The Whiskey Library. The bar is included in The Irish Whiskey Trail. The hotel is also home to Francesca's Restaurant.

_ _/_ _/20_ _

Karma Stone Café Bar

40 Wexford Street, Dublin 2
(1) 478 9455
karmadublin@gmail.com
www.karmastone.ie
A modern bar which opened in 2010, promising 'A new concept in cocktails, funky food and great beers'. It was previously called Bracken's Corner Stone, Corbett's, The Corner Stone, The Junction, McGovern's and Shine. Food is served Monday to Saturday and there is regular entertainment.

_ _/_ _/20_ _

Kehoe's

9 South Anne Street, Dublin 2
(1) 677 8312
johnkehoe@fitzgeraldgroup.ie
www.louisfitzgerald.com
A traditional city centre Victorian heritage pub that is always busy. Many famous Irish writers used to drink here in the past. The pub was first established in 1803 and has traded as Kehoe's since 1903. There is a light snack menu at lunchtime.

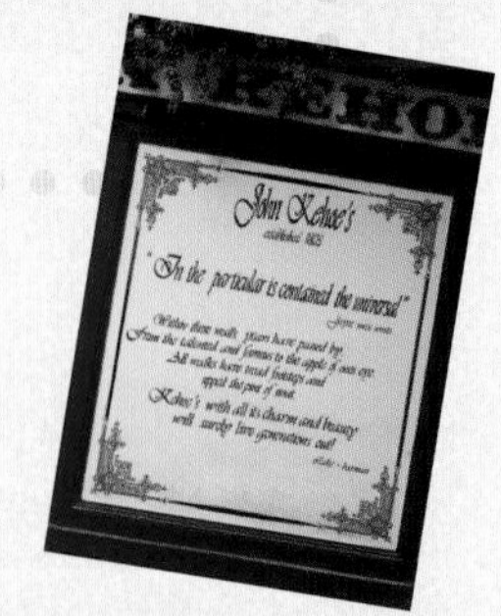

_ _/_ _/20_ _

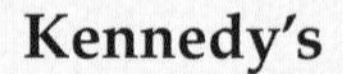

Kennedy's

30–32 Westland Row, Dublin 2
(1) 679 9077
A traditional local pub and club established in 1850 around the corner from Trinity College. They serve food Monday to Saturday, and have regular entertainment in the bar. The Underground Club opens at weekends. The pub was frequented by literary luminaries such as Samuel Beckett and James Joyce.

_ _/_ _/20_ _

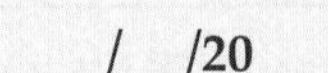

John Kennedy's

10 George's Quay,
Dublin 2
A traditonal city centre pub, next door to Tara Street railway station. It was established circa 1860 and was was restored in 2011. Known as The Railway Bar for a time, it has traded as Kennedy's since 1920.

_ _/_ _/20_ _

Kobra Bar and Restaurant

Leeson Hotel, 26 Lower Leeson Street, Dublin 2
(1) 676 3380
kobra@eircom.net nvnightclub@yahoo.com
www.kobrabar.com
Kobra Bar and Restaurant and NV Nightclub are situated in The Leeson Hotel Dublin. NV Nightclub was previously called Rio's Nightclub. This establishment is currently only trading as a hotel as the bar, restaurant and nightclub are closed.

_ _/_ _/20_ _

Lafayette Café Bar and Terrace

D'Olier Street and Westmoreland Street,
O'Connell Bridge, Dublin 2
(1) 674 6335
A New York-style bar that opened in 2011, also home to Sanctuary Nightclub which opened in the same year. 'Where New York uber cool meets Paris café chic.'
It was previously called Redz and for a short time in 2010 it was The Edge Nightclub. There is regular entertainment.

_ _/_ _/20_ _

Larry Murphy's

43–44 Lower Baggot Street, Dublin 2
(1) 662 4561
A traditional sports bar very much into rugby. It was previously known as Liam Murphy's. The pub was established in 1809. Light snacks are served Monday to Saturday.

_ _/_ _/20_ _

Legends

The Arlington Hotel, 16–18 Lord Edward Street, Dublin 2
(1) 670 8777
stay@arlingtonhoteltemplebar.com
www.legends.ie
The Arlington Hotel which is home to this bar is opposite Dublin Castle. It was established in 1864 and was previously called The Parliament Hotel and contained The Forum Bar. Legends has a huge collection of miniature spirit bottles, which can be seen throughout the room. Food is served every day in Legends and there is live Irish music and dancing seven nights a week. The Arlington is also home to Copper Alley Nightclub, which opened in 2009.

_ _/_ _/20_ _

The Library Bar

The Central Hotel, 1–5 Exchequer Street, Dublin 2
(1) 679 7302
info@centralhotel.ie
www.centralhotel.ie
This little gem is tucked away on the first floor of The Central Hotel. Food is served every day in the bar. The hotel was established in 1887.

_ _/_ _/20_ _

The Lincoln's Inn

18–19 Lincoln Place, Dublin 2
(1) 676 2044
This traditional city centre pub, close to Trinity College, was the meeting place of James Joyce and Nora Barnacle. A light snack menu is served Monday to Saturday. The pub is closed on Sunday.

_ _/_ _/20_ _

The Lombard Bar

44 Pearse Street, Dublin 2
(1) 671 8033
thelombard@thesmithgroup.ie
www.thesmithgroup.ie
A traditional city centre pub, with accommodation, opposite Pearse Street train station. It previously traded under the names Mahaffy's, Murphy's and O'Dwyer Brother's. Food is served every day.

_ _/_ _/20_ _

The Long Hall

51 South Great George's Street, Dublin 2
(1) 475 1590
thelonghall@eircom.net
A traditional pub, first established around 1700, though the present building, which is now listed, dates from 1877. If you are meeting someone in the pub, tell them you will be there at 18.00, as the clock in the centre of the room has been stuck at 17.58 for as long as I can remember! The pub was once owned by Patrick O'Brien until 1966. He willed the pub to his staff, who sold it on after he died. Food is served every day.

_ _/_ _/20_ _

The Long Stone

10–11 Townsend Street, Dublin 2, (1) 671 8102
A traditional city centre pub with a Celtic theme. The pub was named after a long stone or 'stein', probably erected by the Vikings, that stood near this pub for 800 years. A new Long Stone, carved by Cliodhna Cussen, is now on display on the D'Olier Street and College Street traffic island, opposite Trinity College. The pub was previously called Finnegan's, Hynes's and Walsh's. It was established in 1754. Food is served every day and there is regular entertainment.

_ _/_ _/20_ _

Lost Society Lounge and Nightclub

Powerscourt Townhouse Centre, South William Street, Dublin 2
(1) 611 1777
info@lostsociety.ie
www.lostsociety.ie
A lounge and nightclub in the Powerscourt Townhouse Centre. 'Drink, Dine and Dance.' The nightclub is open Wednesday to Saturday. It was previously called Groucho's, Hooray Henry's and Spy, and was home to Wax Nightclub. Food is served everyday and there is regular entertainment.

_ _/_ _/20_ _

Mac Turcaill's

33 Tara Street, Dublin 2
(1) 679 0981
A traditional family-run pub. Askel was the last Norse High King of Dublin (in Irish *Asgall Mac Torcaill*). Food is served every day and there is regular entertainment.

_ _/_ _/20_ _

The Magic Glasses Bar

Stephen's Green Hotel, 1–5 Harcourt Street, Dublin 2
(1) 417 3000
info@ocallaghanhotels.com
www.ocallaghanhotels.com
Hotel bar of the Stephen's Green Hotel, which is actually on Harcourt Street with its entrance on Cuffe Street. Food is served in the bar every day. The hotel also houses the Pie Dish Bistro.

_ _/_ _/20_ _

The Marble Bar

The Westbury Hotel, Harry Street, off Grafton Street, Dublin 2
(1) 679 1122
westbury@doylecollection.com
www.doylecollection.com
The Marble Bar is on the first floor of The Westbury Hotel, just off Grafton Street. It is accessed through the Gallery Lounge. There are many sofas throughout this relaxing lounge. A light snack menu is served every day. The hotel is also home to The Wilde Restaurant on the first floor and Café Novo Bar and Brasserie, located on the ground floor and which has a second entrance in Clarendon Street.

_ _/_ _/20_ _

Matt The Thresher

31–32 Lower Pembroke Street, Dublin 2
(1) 676 2980
matts@ireland.com
www.mattthethresher.ie
A pub which was originally established circa 1830 and opened under its current name in 2010 as a gastro pub. It was previously called Higgins and The Pembroke. There is regular entertainment.

_ _/_ _/20_ _

The Market Bar

14a Fade Street, Dublin 2
(1) 613 9094
info@marketbar.ie
www.marketbar.ie
A gastro pub in a site which was formerly used as a market, and can be entered from the Market Arcade on South Great George's Street. The pub was established in 2003. Food is served seven days a week and the menu includes tapas.

_ _/_ _/20_ _

McDaid's

3 Harry Street, Dublin 2
(1) 679 4395
A traditional city centre pub. It is well known by literary historians, as many famous Irish writers drank and wrote here, even bringing typewriters along with them. The building was at one time a city morgue. It was established in 1779, and has been trading as McDaid's since 1873.

_ _/_ _/20_ _

McGrattan's Café Bar

76 Fitzwilliam Lane, Dublin 2
(1) 661 8808
info@mcgrattans.ie
www.mcgrattans.ie
A traditional pub just off Baggot Street. It was first established as a restaurant in 1979 and opened as a café bar in 2004. There is regular entertainment.

_ _/_ _/20_ _

Mercantile Bar and Grill

The Mercantile Hotel, 25–28 Dame Street and Dame Lane, Dublin 2
(1) 670 7100
sales@mercantilehotel.ie
www.mercantilehotel.ie
At one time this bar was called Oliver Goldsmith's Bar and sections of it were known as Broker's and O'Brien's. It is housed in The Mercantile Hotel, previously called The Trinity Arch Hotel and The Adam's Trinity Hotel. The hotel is also home to The Sing Song Club. Food is served every day and there is entertainment every night.

_ _/_ _/20_ _

The Merchant's Arch Bar and Restaurant

48–49 Wellington Quay, Dublin 2
(1) 607 4010
bookings@merchantsarch.ie
www.merchantsarch.ie

A traditional bar in a building steeped in history. It hosts music sessions daily. It is also home to Brewery Lane which is in the Parlour Room. The pub used to be a kebab shop, and before this it was The River Club. From 1908 until 1980 it was a shirt factory. However, most famously, as you will see on the backdrop of the bar, it was 'The Guild Hall of Merchant Tailors which was established here in 1821'. It opened in its current form in 2010. Food is served every day and there is traditional music most nights.

_ _/_ _/20_ _

Messrs Maguire

Burgh Quay, Dublin 2
(1) 670 5777
info@messrsmaguire.ie
www.messrsmaguire.ie
A micro brewery, pub and café bar with five bars over four floors: The Brewery Bar, The Cellar Bar, The Liffey Bar, The Main Bar and The Old Library Bar, the upper floors reached by an impressive wooden staircase. They serve 'uniquely hand-crafted beer brewed on the premises of M M Brew House.' The pub was established in 1808. Food is served every day and there is regular entertainment.

_ _/_ _/20_ _

The Mezz Bar

The Riverhouse Hotel, 24 Eustace Street, Dublin 2
(1) 670 7655
reservations@riverhousehotel.com
www.riverhousehotel.com
The Mezz Bar in The Riverhouse Hotel has live music seven nights a week. The hotel also houses The Mezz Venue and The Industry Club and Venue, previously called Think Tank Nightclub.

_ _/_ _/20_ _

The Mint Bar

The Westin Hotel, Westmoreland Street, Dublin 2
(1) 645 1322
reservationsdublin@westin.com
www.themintbar.ie
The Mint Bar, downstairs in the Westin Hotel, used to be bank vaults. The hotel restaurant, the Exchange, and cocktail bar are on the ground floor. Afternoon tea is served in The Atrium Lounge on the first floor. It is an enclosed courtyard in the centre of the hotel with a glass roof five floors overhead.

_ _/_ _/20_ _

The Morgan Bar

The Morgan Hotel, 10 Fleet Street, Dublin 2
(1) 643 7000
bar@themorgan.com
www.themorgan.com
Bar and club of The Morgan Hotel in the heart of Temple Bar. A great place for cocktails. Food is served every day and there is regular entertainment.

_ _/_ _/20_ _

Mulligan's of Poolbeg Street

8 Poolbeg Street, Dublin 2
(1) 677 5582
mulligansp oolbegstreet@eircom.net
www.mulligans.ie
One of Dublin's best-loved traditional pubs, renowned for good beer: 'The home of the pint'. James Joyce was once a regular and John F. Kennedy visited in 1945. The pub was established in 1782 and prior to that it was a shebeen (an unlicensed drinking venue).

_ _/_ _/20_ _

Neary's Bar

1 Chatham Street, Dublin 2
(1) 677 8596
A traditional city centre Victorian pub situated near St Stephen's Green. The pub is often used by the stars and visitors to the nearby Gaiety Theatre. In past times actors often entered the pub through Tangier Lane between the pub and theatre. A light snack menu is served Monday to Saturday.

_ _/_ _/20_ _

Ned's of Townsend Street

44 Townsend Street, Dublin 2
(1) 677 9507
Ned Scanlon's traditional local early house near Tara Street railway station. This pub, which offers regular entertainment, was previously called Kennedy's. It was established in 1861.

_ _/_ _/20_ _

No 1 Merrion Street

Mont Clare Hotel, 1 Merrion Square, Dublin 2
(1) 607 3800
info@ocallaghanhotels.com
www.ocallaghanhotels.com
A traditional hotel bar. Lunch is served on weekdays. The Mont Clare Hotel is made up of four Grade A listed Georgian houses, one of which was the Duke of Wellington's birthplace. The hotel also houses Goldsmith's Restaurant.

_ _/_ _/20_ _

The No Name Bar

Kelly's Hotel, 3 Fade Street, Dublin 2
(1) 764 5681
www.kellysdublin.com
A modern bar on the first floor of Kelly's Hotel. It has an array of interesting furniture and other items, including a safe which was used by the manager of the market in Fade Street who had an office here. The bar is known by many names—The Bar With No Name, Number 3, The Secret Bar, The Slug, and The Snail. Food is served at weekends. L'Gueuleton restaurant is on the ground floor. The Candle Bar is the hotel residents' bar.

_ _/_ _/20_ _

O'Connell's

29 South Richmond Street, Dublin 2
A traditional old-style local pub. It has traded as O'Connell's since circa 1935 and was Hughes' beforehand. The pub has been run by the O'Byrne family since 1971. Many film scenes have been shot here, as well as the TV series *Raw*.

_ _/_ _/20_ _

The Octagon Bar

The Clarence Hotel, 6–8 Wellington Quay, Dublin 2
(1) 407 0800
reservations@theclarence.ie
www.theclarence.ie www.thekitchennightclub.com
Cocktail bar in The Clarence Hotel, which is owned by Bono and The Edge. The hotel also houses The Kitchen Nightclub and Tea Room Restaurant which is set in the original ballroom of the hotel. The Kitchen's entrance is in Essex Street East, next to the hotel's back door. There is regular entertainment in the bar.

THE KITCHEN

_ _/_ _/20_ _

The Odeon Bar and Grill

Old Harcourt Station, 57 Harcourt Street, Dublin 2
A bar and grill situated in what used to be the Harcourt Street railway station, transformed in 1999 into one of Dublin's finest bars. This establishment is currently closed.

_ _/_ _/20_ _

O'Donoghue's of Merrion Row

15 Merrion Row (off Baggot Street),
Dublin 2, (1) 660 7194
odonoghuesdublin@eircom.net,
www.odonoghues.ie

A great traditional music bar, a favourite of Christy Moore and many other singers and musicians over the years. There are photos and drawings of famous musicians throughout, and outside on the fascia is a Rock 'N' Stroll Trail plaque dedicated to The Dubliners—the group formed here in 1962 in the back bar. The pub was established in 1789 and has been trading as O'Donoghue's since 1934. There is music here every night, often with more than one session playing at the same time in different sections of the bar. A light snack menu is served every day. A second bar, set over two floors, opened in 2010 and is finished in a traditional style. O'Donoghue's also has guest accommodation.

_ _/_ _/20_ _

Beer Garden & Lounges
Food available all day

Oil Can Harry's

31–32 Lower Mount Street, Dublin 2
(1) 661 1828
contact@oilcanharrys.ie
www.oilcanharrys.ie

An old style public house, established in 1913, popular with the after-work crowd and a good place for sport. There are many sporting pictures around the house. James Joyce was a regular imbiber here. It was previously called The Head Office, Hynes and The Other Place. Food is served every day.

_ _/_ _/20_ _

O'Donoghue's of Suffolk Street

15 Suffolk Street, Dublin 2
(1) 677 0605

A traditional city centre pub. 'Great pints and friendly craic.' Food is served every day and there is entertainment most nights. The interior was created from old timbers from demolished buildings and churches. The site of the pub is of historical importance as it was recorded as a gathering point for early Viking settlers. Its previous names were Thing Mote, Suffolk Lounge / Inn and The Coal Hole.

_ _/_ _/20_ _

The Old Stand

37 Exchequer Street, Dublin 2
(1) 677 7220
www.theoldstandpub.com
A traditional city centre bar, established in 1669 and 'probably the oldest pub in Dublin'. It used to be called Monnico. The pub was named after the old stand in Lansdowne Road. Food is served every day.

_ _/_ _/20_ _

The Old Storehouse Bar and Restaurant

3a Crown Alley, Dublin 2, (1) 607 4003
info@theoldstorehouse.ie, www.theoldstorehouse.ie
A bar and restaurant, opened in 2010 in a former warehouse: 'A. Oman and Son's Household Removal Contractors and Warehousemen'. The pub was previously known as Eamonn Doran's, The Rock Garden and most recently, 3 Crown Alley. The Cranberries played their first gig here as recorded in the plaque. The interior has lots of bric-a-brac and pictures. The pub also houses Madonna's Nightclub which is a separate venture.

_ _/_ _/20_ _

Oliver St John Gogarty

58–59 Fleet Street, Dublin 2
(1) 671 1822
info@gogartys.ie
www.gogartys.ie
A traditional Irish bar and restaurant in the heart of Temple Bar, established in 1835. It also offers accommodation. The 'indoor outdoor' smoking area is well-sheltered from the elements. The pub incorporates The Left Bank bar and The Library Bar. Food is served every day and there is entertainment every day from 2.30 pm.

_ _/_ _/20_ _

O'Neill's of Pearse Street

36–37 Pearse Street, Dublin 2
(1) 671 4074
oneillspub@iol.ie, www.oneillsdublin.com
A Victorian pub and townhouse with guest accommodation, 'A pub with rooms'. The pub was established in 1823 and has traded as O'Neill's since circa 1892. A pub called The O'Neills Crowing Cock used to trade at No 37 Pearse Street. Food is served on weekdays.

_ _/_ _/20_ _

O'Neill's of Suffolk Street

2 Suffolk Street, Dublin 2
(1) 679 3656
mike@oneillsbar.com
www.oneillsbar.com
A traditional city centre bar and restaurant, established circa 1710 and trading as O'Neill's since 1927. 'One of Dublin's most famous and historic pubs' it is renowned for its ageless character, with its numerous alcoves, snugs, nooks and crannies. O'Neill's is included in The Irish Whiskey Trail, and stocks a large selection of craft beers. There is food every day and regular entertainment.

_ _/_ _/20_ _

O'Sullivan's

11–12 Westmoreland Street, Dublin 2,
A traditional city centre pub close to O'Connell Bridge and Trinity College. It is housed within Fleet Street Hotel, formerly Bewley's Hotel. The pub itself was previously Bewley's Café, The Bridge Bar and Trivia Nightclub. Food is served every day.

_ _/_ _/20_ _

O'Reillys

Luke Street, Dublin 2
(1) 671 6769
info@oreillys.ie
www.oreillys.ie
A trendy modern-meets-traditional pub, home to Club Hell, 'Ireland's Biggest Saturday Rock Night'. The pub is built within the arches of Tara Street railway station. Food is served every day and there is regular entertainment. O'Reillys claim they are 'Dublin's Best Kept Secret—Until Now.'

_ _/_ _/20_ _

The Palace Bar

21 Fleet Street, Dublin 2
(1) 671 7388
info@thepalacebar.com
www.thepalacebar.com

A traditional old city centre pub, the gateway to Temple Bar, established in 1823. 'Internationally famous for our intellectual refreshment.' Behind the bar a sign reads: 'A bird is known for its song, A man by his conversation'. The Palace Bar used to be the haunt of journalists from the then nearby *Irish Times* and other well-known Irish writers. The pub stocks over 100 whiskeys and is on The Irish Whiskey Trail. Food is served every day and there is regular entertainment with extra nights over the summer.

_ _/_ _/20_ _

The Pavilion Bar

Trinity College Dublin, College Green, Dublin 2
(1) 896 1279

A bar in the College Park area of Trinity College, mostly used by students and known to them as The Pav. Food is served Mondays to Saturdays. It's pleasant to walk through Trinity College soaking up the college atmosphere and then to have a pint with the students.

_ _/_ _/20_ _

Peadar Kearney's

64 Dame Street, Dublin 2
info@peadarkearneys.com
www.peadarkearneys.com

A traditional city centre pub, named after Peader Kearney, who composed *Amhrán na bhFiann* (the Soldier's Song), the Irish national anthem. The Kearney family tree is on display in the bar. The pub was previously called Rouge Bar and Nightclub. There is regular entertainment.

_ _/_ _/20_ _

The Pearse Tavern

81–82 Pearse Street, Dublin 2
padraicpearse@gmail.com

A traditional local pub and early house situated on the edge of the city centre. It was previously called Moroney's. There is regular entertainment.

_ _/_ _/20_ _

Peter's Pub Bar and Snug

1 Johnson's Place, Dublin 2
(1) 679 3347
www.peterspub.ie
A traditional city centre pub with no TV and no music—just conversation. Their slogan is 'Best drinks in good company'. A light snack menu is served every day.

_ _/_ _/20_ _

The Porterhouse Central

45–47 Nassau Street, Dublin 2
(1) 677 4180
www.porterhousebrewco.com
A traditional-meets-modern bar opposite Trinity College. It is interconnected to Lillie's Bordello nightclub. The pub was previously called The Bernie Inn and Judge Roy Beans. Food is served every day and there is entertainment most nights.

_ _/_ _/20_ _

The Porterhouse Temple Bar

16–18 Parliament Street, Dublin 2
(1) 679 8847
www.porterhousebrewco.com
A large pub with two bars over four floors. It opened in 1996 and is said to have the largest range of bottled beers in Ireland. Food is served every day and live bands play most nights.

_ _/_ _/20_ _

The Portobello Hotel Bar

33 South Richmond Street, Dublin 2
(1) 475 2715
info@portobellohotel.ie
www.portobellohotel.ie
A traditional local hotel bar and home to Rain Nightclub. This hotel was established in 1806. It is situated next to The Grand Canal and Latouche Bridge, which dates back to 1791. Food is served every day in the bar and there is regular entertainment.

_ _/_ _/20_ _

Presidents' Bar

Davenport Hotel, Merrion Square, Dublin 2
(1) 607 3500
info@ocallaghanhotels.com
www.ocallaghanhotels.com
This bar in The Davenport Hotel has a picture gallery of presidents from different countries and organisations. Food is served every day. The hotel is also home to Lanyon's Restaurant.

_ _/_ _/20_ _

The Purty Kitchen

East Essex Street, Dublin 2
Previously called Bad Bob's and Bob's this modern bar, club and music venue is currently closed. It includes The Sycamore nightclub on the top floor and The Marquee Club on the first floor. The building dates back to 1879.

_ _/_ _/20_ _

The Quays

11–12 Temple Bar Square, Dublin 2
(1) 671 3922
thequaysdublin@fitzgeraldgroup.com
www.louisfitzgerald.com/quaystemplebar
A traditional Irish music bar and Irish restaurant. The music, which is in four acts, starts at 3.30 pm every day. This pub was previously called The Crane.

_ _/_ _/20_ _

Pygmalion Public House and Café

Powerscourt Townhouse Centre, South William Street, Dublin 2, (1) 633 4479
info@pyg.ie, www.pyg.ie
A modern bar, restaurant and nightclub, previously called Ba Mizu. It has traded as Pygmalion since 2009. Food is served every day and there is entertainment most nights.

_ _/_ _/20_ _

Rush Bar

65 South William Street, Dublin 2
(1) 671 9542
rushbar@eircom.net
A modern city centre pub established in 2004. A light snack menu is served every day.

_ _/_ _/20_ _

SamSara

La Stampa Hotel, 35–36 Dawson Street, Dublin 2
(1) 677 4444
hotel@lastampa.ie
www.lastampa.ie
This Moroccan-themed bar, housed within La Stampa Hotel, is a great place for cocktails. Food is served Monday to Saturday and there is regular entertainment. The hotel also has two restaurants.

_ _/_ _/20_ _

Sheehan's

17 Chatham Street/Chatham Row, Dublin 2
(1) 677 1914
A traditional family-run city centre pub just off Grafton Street. The pub was established in 1933 by Jerry Sheehan. Food is served every day and there is occasional entertainment.

_ _/_ _/20_ _

Scruffy Murphy's

1–2 Powers Court off Lower Mount Street, Dublin 2
(1) 661 5006
A well-hidden traditional local pub just off Lower Mount street dating from the early 1900s. It was previously called The Beehive, as at one time there was a beehive on the side of the building. It was also called Seán P. Murphy's. Food is served on weekdays.

_ _/_ _/20_ _

Sinnott's

South King Street, Dublin 2, (1) 478 4698
bookings@sinnotts.ie, www.sinnotts.ie
A traditional pub just off Grafton Street. It has a large collection of original literary pictures and prints by Irish artists and writers. There is a bar in the centre of the room, which is known as an island bar. The pub is also very much into sport. Sinnott's was established in 1989. Another pub, called Sinnot's (note the different spelling), was situated on a nearby site many years ago. Sinnott's serves food every day and offers regular entertainment.

_ _/_ _/20_ _

JJ Smyth's

12 Aungier Street, Dublin 2
(1) 475 2565
info@jjsmyths.com
www.jjsmyths.com
A traditional local city centre pub and music venue also known as JJ's. Upstairs is home to 'Dublin's Premier Live Jazz and Blues Venue'. This building was the birthplace of Irish poet and playwright Thomas Moore, whose plaque is under the window. It was previously called T. Brady's, O'Looney's, Rathigan's and Thomas Moore House. The pub was established in 1730.

_ _/_ _/20_ _

Solas

31 Wexford Street, Dublin 2, (1) 478 0583
info@solasbars.com, www.solasbars.com
A 'funky drinking bar and restaurant' Solas (meaning 'light' in Irish) is an award-winning cocktail bar spread over three floors. It was previously called Carew's Bar and was established as Solas in the 1990s. There is entertainment most nights.

_ _/_ _/20_ _

The South William

52 South William Street, Dublin 2
An urban lounge and bar in the city centre. This establishment is currently closed.

_ _/_ _/20_ _

Speak Easy Café Bar

4 South George's Street, Dublin 2
(01) 6778096
info@speakeasycafebar.ie
www.speakeasycafebar.ie
A city centre pub full of old furniture and other items that now decorate the pub in a very creative way. It was previously called Shebeen Chic. Food is served every day and there is entertainment most nights.

_ _/_ _/20_ _

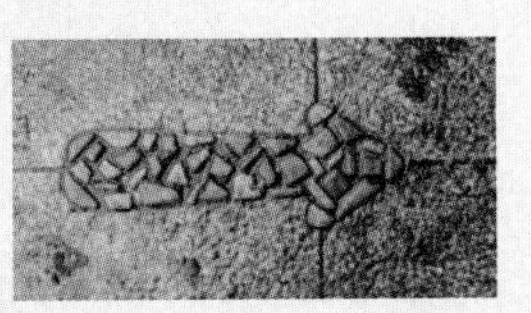

The Stag's Head

1 Dame Court, Dublin 2
(1) 679 3687
www.louisfitzgerald.com
A heritage pub, established in the early 18th century, full of character and characters, with fine timberwork and mirrors throughout. Many films have been shot here, including *Educating Rita* and more recently *Michael Collins*. The three rooms are called The Snug, The Parlour Bar and The Stag's Tail. At one time the pub was known as Tyson's; it still bears this name on the clock outside. Back in the 1830s it was called John Bull's Albion Hotel and Tavern. I am told that this was the first pub in Dublin to convert to electric lighting.

_ _/_ _/20_ _

Stil Bar and Lounge

The Hilton Hotel, Charlemont Place, Dublin 2
(1) 402 9988
www.hilton.com
This modern hotel bar was previously called The Champion Sports Bar. The Hilton Hotel is beside the Grand Canal near Charlemont Bridge. It also houses The Uisce Restaurant. Food is served every day in the bar and there is regular entertainment.

_ _/_ _/20_ _

The Swan (Lynch's)

58 Aungier Street, Dublin 2
(1) 475 2722
info@swanbar.com
An old traditional local pub on the edge of the city centre. Scenes from the film *The Courier* with Gabriel Byrne were filmed here, as were various TV commercials. It was previously called Maher's and O'Reilly's. The Swan boasts a secret door which was used as an escape route during the Civil War. The pub dates back to 1723. A light snack menu is served Monday to Saturday and there is occasional entertainment.

_ _/_ _/20_ _

Sweeney's

Le Cirk Boutique Hotel, 32 Dame Street and Dame Lane, Dublin 2
(1) 635 0056
shauna.sweeneys@gmail.com
www.sweeneysdublin.com
A city centre bar, previously called Le Cirk Bar, housed within Le Cirk Boutique Hotel. The Basement Bar, previously called La Basement, and the first floor bar open at weekends. Food is served every day and there is entertainment most nights.

_ _/_ _/20_ _

The Temple Bar Pub

47–48 Temple Bar, Dublin 2
(1) 672 5287
info@thetemplebarpub.com
www.thetemplebarpub.com
A traditional city centre pub first licensed in 1819. The house stocks Ireland's largest whiskey collection, with approximately 450 bottles of Irish, Scotch and bourbons available at the bar. The pub is on The Irish Whiskey Trail. Food is served every day and there are traditional music sessions every day.

_ _/_ _/20_ _

TGI Friday's Fleet Street

19–20 Fleet Street, Dublin 2, (1) 672 8975
www.fridays.ie
A branch of the American restaurant and bar chain, opened in 2012 in The Fleet Street Hotel, formerly Bewley's Hotel. The interior is filled with interesting items which include various kinds of automobile, musical and sports memorabilia.

_ _/_ _/20_ _

TGI Friday's Stephen's Green

2 St Stephen's Green Centre, Dublin 2
(1) 478 1233
info@fridays.ie
www.fridays.ie
A branch of the American restaurant and bar chain.
'In here, it's always Friday'.

_ _/_ _/20_ _

Thunder Road Café

52–57 Fleet Street, Dublin 2, (1) 679 4057
www.thunderroadcafe.com
An American-style cocktail bar and restaurant, with a motorcycle theme — there are Harley Davidsons on display in the restaurant. There is regular entertainment in the bar.

_ _/_ _/20_ _

Thomas Read The Oak

82 Dame Street, Dublin 2
(1) 671 7283 (1) 671 8267
This is two pubs in one. Thomas Read is the newer section, opened in 1993, and named after an old cutlers', Dublin's oldest shop, that traded a few doors down. This bar was previously an art gallery. The oak-panelled interior of the older section, The Oak Bar, came from the original fittings of RMS *Mauretania* which was decommissioned circa 1940. The pub was once home to The Transformer Club which is currently closed. Up to the 1950s The Oak was known as Humphry's.

_ _/_ _/20_ _

Toner's

139 Lower Baggot Street, Dublin 2
(1) 676 3090
Toner's Museum Bar is an old traditional city pub full of character. It is what it says on the sign outside: A Pub. It was established in 1818 and is housed in a building which dates back to 1734. In 2010 it won the award of Ireland's Best Snug. As far as we know, this is the only pub in Dublin where W. B. Yeats ever had a drink. A light snack menu is served at lunchtime.

_ _/_ _/20_ _

Trinity Bar and Venue

Citi Hotel, 46–49 Dame Street, Dublin 2
(1) 679 4455
reservations@dublincitihotel.com
www.dublincitihotel.com
Bar and venue of Citi Hotel. It styles itself 'The only Irish-style tapas bar in Ireland'. It is a good lively spot with entertainment most nights. Citi Hotel is also home to Havana Night Club. The club was previously called Citi Club and Jim Joe's.

_ _/_ _/20_ _

The Trinity Inn

37b Pearse Street, Dublin 2
(1) 671 4074
oneillspub@iol.ie
www.oneillsdublin.com
A traditional city centre pub. It was previously called Benshaw's and Slattery's. Lunch is served on weekdays.

_ _/_ _/20_ _

The Turk's Head

The Paramount Hotel, 27–30 Parliament Street, Dublin 2
(1) 417 9900
reservations@paramounthotel.ie
www.paramounthotel.ie
A city centre bar, housed within The Paramount Hotel, renowned for its extravagant design, which includes mosaics and Spanish-style architecture. The large music bar opens late every night. The pub was established in 1760 and was previously called The Parliament. Food is served every day.

_ _/_ _/20_ _

Ukiyo Bar

7–9 Exchequer Street, Dublin 2
(1) 633 4071
info@ukiyobar.com, www.ukiyobar.com
A sake bar and Japanese restaurant, renowned for its four karaoke booths in the basement. These booths, which can hold ten patrons each, have a list of 30,000 songs. The booths have phones connected to the bar, so singers can order drinks.

_ _/_ _/20_ _

The Vertigo Bar

The Maldron Hotel, Cardiff Lane, Dublin 2
(1) 643 9500
info.cardifflane@maldronhotels.com
www.maldronhotels.com
Hotel bar of The Maldron Hotel, which is near the Bord Gáis Energy Theatre. Food is served in the bar every day. The hotel is also home to The Stir Restaurant.

_ _/_ _/20_ _

The Village

26 Wexford Street, Dublin 2
(1) 475 8555
www.thevillagevenue.com
A city centre bar and music venue with entertainment most nights, and food served Monday to Saturday. It was previously called Mono.

_ _/_ _/20_ _

Whelan's

23–25 Wexford Street, Dublin 2
(1) 478 0766
info@whelanslive.com
www.whelanslive.com
A traditional bar with two music venues. The smaller one is upstairs and the larger one is reached by an entrance around the corner. The current house was built in 1894 and Whelan's opened here in 1990. One section of the pub, no. 25, was previously called Burke's Pub and was also known as Kevin's Port. A pub on this site was established by Christopher Brady circa 1772. There is entertainment every night.

_ _/_ _/20_ _

The Windjammer

111 Townsend Street, Dublin 2
A traditional local pub and early house, named after a kind of large sailing ship with an iron or steel hull, built to carry cargo in the late 19th and early 20th centuries. It is just two minutes' walk from the Seán O'Casey pedestrian swingbridge on the River Liffey, which was built in 2005. The pub was established in 1928 and was restored to its original style in 2010. There is regular entertainment.

_ _/_ _/20_ _

Winners' Bar

Alexander Hotel, Fenian Street, Dublin 2
(1) 607 3700
alexandergm@ocallaghanhotel.com
www.ocallaghanhotels.com
The bar of The Alexander Hotel, which is also home to Caravaggio's Restaurant. Food is served in the bar every day.

_ _/_ _/20_ _

The Workman's Club

10 Wellington Quay, Dublin 2
(1) 670 6692
info@theworkmansclub.com
www.theworkmansclub.com
This pub and venue was previously home to a private working-man's club. The fine building with its old-style traditional bars lay vacant for many years before opening under its current title in 2010. There is entertainment most nights.

_ _/_ _/20_ _

Northside suburbs

Dublin 3: Ballybough, North Strand, Clonliffe, Clontarf, Dollymount, East Wall, Fairview, most of Killester and Marino

Ballybough is a mainly working-class district. It is the birthplace of Luke Kelly of the Dubliners and the film director Jim Sheridan.

North Strand was devastated during the Second World War—German aircraft veered off course and released bombs over the area.

Clonliffe is best known for Holy Cross College, Dublin's Catholic seminary.

Part of Clontarf is on the coast. Clontarf Castle, a few minutes' walk from the seashore, is famous as a key location of the Battle of Clontarf in 1014, in which the Irish drove away the Vikings. There has been a castle on the site since 1172. In modern times, it has functioned as a bar, cabaret venue, and hotel. More recently this area has become famous for the fact that Bono went to Clontarf's Mount Temple Comprehensive School, where he met his future wife and the future members of U2.

Part of Dublin 3 includes a section of Bull Island, an island in Dublin Bay. It is a designated nature reserve. It is also home to Dollymount Strand, a 5-km long beach, which is a popular walking and recreational area for Dubliners.

East Wall is an inner city area, mainly residential. It dates back to the eighteenth century. Originally a working-class neighbourhood, in recent years it has developed because of the addition of the IFSC and other new businesses.

Fairview is also a coastal district, part of which consists of reclaimed land from the sea. On of the area's main features is Fairview Park, which covers approximately 50 acres.

Killester is a small mainly residential area located between Clontarf, Donnycarney, Raheny and Artane. It has a shopping plaza and Killester's third-level College of Further Education. Marino is a residential suburb.

The Casino at Marino, situated in the gardens of Marino House, is widely regarded as the most important neo-classical building in Ireland. "Casino" means "little house", and it is an apt name, for the building is built with the proportions of a much bigger and grander building—but in miniature! The effect is most unsettling, and has to be seen to be believed.

Dublin 5 : most of Artane, Coolock (other parts of Coolock are in Dublin 13 and 17), Harmonstown, Kilbarrack, Raheny and Edenmore.

Artane is home to the Artane Boys Band which famously plays before big matches in Croke Park. Artane Castle Shopping Centre is named after Artane Castle, whose ruins were taken down in 1825. Artane House was erected on its site.

Within Coolock is Northside Shopping Centre.

Harmonstown is a small suburb located between Artane and Raheny.

Kilbarrack residential suburb runs inland from the coast. It was historically an area of fields, many being lands held by church establishments. Today Kilbarrack is well known for its sporting clubs and teams.

Raheny is well known for St Anne's Park, a public park and recreational facility. Covering over 270 acres, it is the second largest public park in Dublin. Phoenix Park is the first. A small area of the park falls into Clontarf and Dollymount.

Edenmore is a locality within Raheny, with several housing developments and a large municipal park.

Dublin 7: Smithfield, Cabra, Grangegorman, Phibsborough, Ashtown and Stoneybatter.

Jameson Distillery is located in Bow Street, Smithfield. Visitors are invited to join a tour where they will see how whiskey is made. Also on site is a gift shop, restaurant and bars. Smithfield has been recently rejuvenated and restored. It is mainly known for its horse market, a lively affair held once a month on Sundays. The Four Courts is Ireland's main courts building. It was built in the late 1700s by renowned architect James Gandon. During the Civil War, the Public Records Office was destroyed by a huge explosion. There are still visible bullet holes on the exterior of the building that date from this conflict. The Dublin Criminal Court of Justice opened in January 2010, replacing the Four Courts and other buildings as the location for criminal trials.

Much of Cabra was built in the 1940s as part of a public housing programme. Before this, the area was mostly open countryside. Famous former residents include actors Angeline Ball and Michael Gambon, world champion boxer Steve Collins, Irish football player and manager Johnny Giles and singer Dickie

Rock. Cabra has also been home to the well-known Batchelors factory since 1935.

Grangegorman is best known as the location of St Brendan's Hospital, which was historically the main psychiatric hospital serving the greater Dublin region.

One of Phibsborough's most prominent and impressive features is St Peter's Church, built in the early nineteenth century. Its stained glass windows are particularly noteworthy. The district of Phibsborough retains many of its original Victorian red-brick houses, and in recent years Phibsborough has undergone much renewal.

Ashtown is a suburb flanked by Castleknock to the west, Cabra to the east and Finglas to the North.

Stoneybatter was originally known as *Bóther na gCloch*, the road of the stones. At that time it was a country road, and a thoroughfare to Dublin for those travelling from the west and north-west. It used to be well-known for its nearby cattle market, which has now been developed into residential housing. In recent years the streets and areas around Stoneybatter have been used as locations for the TV series *Dear Sarah* and *Lost*, and the films *Michael Collins* and *Angela's Ashes.*

Dublin 9: Beaumont, Drumcondra, part of Glasnevin, Santry, Whitehall, Donnycarney and parts of Ballymun.

Beaumont was the home of the original Guinness family from 1764 to 1855. This residence is now Beaumont Convalescent Home. One of Ireland's largest hospitals, Beaumont Hospital, is located here.

Croke Park, located between Drumcondra and Ballybough, is the principal stadium and headquarters of the GAA (Gaelic Athletic Association), Ireland's biggest sporting organisation.

Santry is a residential suburb and home to Santry Demesne, a public park with features such as a pond, an arboretum, and abundant wildlife.

Whitehall is a residential area on the outskirts of the city centre. It takes its name from a house called White Hall, which used to be located to the south of the village. Luke Kelly of the Dubliners used to live in Whitehall and there is a stone in the area dedicated to him.

Donnycarney is a mainly residential area. It is most notable for Parnell Park, a GAA stadium. It was the birthplace of Paddy Moloney of the Chieftains and former Taoiseach Charles Haughey.

Dublin 11: Finglas, Meakstown, most of Glasnevin and most of Ballymun.

Much of Finglas consists of extensive housing estates. The town is still expanding, with large private developments being built around the village. It is the home of many notable figures, including actor Colm Meaney, comedian Brendan O'Carroll, and writer and poet Dermot Bolger.

Meakstown is a residential area located mostly within Finglas.

The National Botanic Gardens are located in Glasnevin, and cover an area of 27 acres. Over the years they have developed to hold 20,000 living plants and millions of dried plant specimens. The gardens include glasshouses of architectural importance, namely the Palm House and the Curvilinear Range. Glasnevin Cemetery is the largest cemetery in Ireland. It is the resting place for a host of historical figures, including Michael Collins, Charles Stewart Parnell and Arthur Griffith. In 2010, an excellent museum opened in the cemetery.

Ballymun was once known for the Ballymun flats, multi-storey buildings which became a symbol of poverty, drug abuse and social problems. With nearly all the towers now demolished, Ballymun has undergone a major regeneration. Many of its previous residents are now living in new and better houses, and new parks and other amenities have also been introduced.

Dublin 13: Bayside, Baldoyle, Donaghmede, Portmarnock, Sutton and the Ayrfield part of Coolock.

Bayside is situated close to the sea and was built in the 1970s, around a central shopping and civic area. Former residents of Bayside include Ronan Keating of Boyzone and Fergal O'Brien, snooker player.

Baldoyle is a small coastal village. It now also contains many housing estates and is home to the Baldoyle Industrial Estate.

Before its development into a suburb, Donaghmede was mostly farmland, with several large houses and small cottages. The area is also home to the Donaghmede Shopping Centre.

Portmarnock is known for its long narrow beach, which is nicknamed the Velvet Strand due to its smooth sand. It has extensive housing estates to the north and west of the town.

Sutton is a neighbour to Howth. On the coast at Sutton is a tombolo connecting Howth to the mainland. Sutton is surrounded by many beaches, and it also has a golf club and rugby club.

Ayrfield is a locality containing several housing estates and a large industrial estate. It is near Donaghmede and Darndale.

Dublin 15: Castleknock, Carpenterstown, Blanchardstown, Clonsilla, Coolmine, Corduff, Mulhuddart and Tyrellstown

Castleknock was a rural village until the late 1960s. Housing estates then began to be developed and the village grew into a suburb of Dublin. Persons of note who come from Castleknock include actor Colin Farrell and Eamonn Coghlan, former Olympic athlete.

Carpenterstown is a suburb situated next to Castleknock.

Blanchardstown has had a similar history to Castleknock in that it developed and extended its residential housing in the same time period. Blanchardstown Shopping Centre is a vast complex that stretches over 107 acres. This area also includes a medical centre, library and more.

Clonsilla is a large residential suburb, with many housing estates developed over recent years. Clonsilla contains Luttrellstown Castle, once owned by members of the Guinness family and now a hotel. Also in the area is The Shackleton Gardens, a famous walled garden located at Beech Park, a public park, which was opened in 2009.

Coolmine is a suburb which is located around 14 km from the city centre. It has a large sports centre, the Coolmine Sports Complex.

Corduff's name has changed quite a lot over the centuries. Back in the sixteenth century it was Culduff, later Colduff, then Corduffe, Courtduffe and finally its present name. Its amenities include a shopping centre, a sports centre and the Corduff Community Youth Project.

Mulhuddart is a residential suburb, with extensive housing developments. Its name means 'The Hill of the Milking Place'. Several old church and old house ruins are still standing in the area.

Tyrellstown is a rapidly expanding suburb. The Tyrellstown Town Centre was opened in 2005 and more retail outlets are being planned to cater for the growing population.

Dublin 17: Balgriffin, most of Coolock (apart from Ayrfield which is in Dublin 13), Clonshaugh, Corballis, Ballygall, Priorswood, Darndale, Northern Cross and Clarehall.

Balgriffin is currently changing from a rural area into a residential suburb of Dublin. It is situated about 6 km from the city centre. It used to be the home of the historic Belcamp College, which was burned down in 2011.

Coolock was a small village until around the 1950s, when it began to be developed. It now consists of many housing estates. Coolock Industrial Estate has a range of businesses, and the headquarters of Cadburys Ireland is here. Coolock includes the following localities: Clonshaugh, which stretches from Clonshaugh Industrial Estate to close to Basking Lane, and has a high density of residential housing; Priorswood, which is also a highly populated locality and is found between Darndale and Clonshaugh; Corballis; and Ballygall.

Darndale has a high concentration of social housing. It was originally farmland in the northern part of Coolock. One of Darndale's features is a fishing pond, built in cooperation with the Eastern Regional Fisheries Board.

Northern Cross is a modern complex situated on the Malahide road. It comprises retail stores, office accommodation and residential apartments. It is also home to a four-star Hilton Hotel.

Clarehall is a residential area. A recent development is the Clare Hall Shopping Centre.

Annesley House

70 North Strand Road, North Strand, Dublin 3
(1) 855 5121
A traditional local pub close to Croke Park, previously called Chaser's and Grainger's. The pub also bears the name A. Ó hEachthairin, which is the Irish equivalent of 'A. Ahearn'. There is regular entertainment.

_ _/_ _/20_ _

Bar Code

Clontarf Road, Clontarf, Dublin 3
A very large bar and club with American pool tables, a games room, a climbing wall, novelty golf and lots more. This establishment was closed in 2010.

_ _/_ _/20_ _

The Bram Stoker

225 Clontarf Road, Clontarf, Dublin 3
(1) 833 2680
This traditional bar is located on the coast road next to Clontarf Yacht and Boat Club. It was previously The Clontarf Court Hotel. Food is served every day and there is also accommodation. Bram Stoker, author of *Dracula*, lived in Clontarf in the late 19th century.

_ _/_ _/20_ _

The Bridge Tavern

6 Summerhill Parade, Summerhill, Dublin 3
A traditional local pub, with regular entertainment. It is known locally as Bermo's, a nickname derived from its previous name, Bermingham's.

_ _/_ _/20_ _

Harry Byrne's

107 Howth Road, Clontarf, Dublin 3
(1) 833 2650
A traditional local pub which has been well extended over recent years by the Byrnes, who salvaged old building materials nationwide and from Europe to complement its original style. Previously known as Corbett's, the pub was established in 1798 and has been trading as Byrne's since circa 1940. It has one of the best beer gardens on the north side of the city.

_ _/_ _/20_ _

Clonliffe House (Brady and Gorman)

44 Ballybough Road, Ballybough, Dublin 3
(1) 855 6477
A traditional local pub near Croke Park. It was previously called McCann's and The Fluter Good. A light snack menu is served and there is regular entertainment.

_ _/_ _/20_ _

Connolly's The Sheds

198 Clontarf Road, Clontarf, Dublin 3, (1) 833 8691
Trading as Connolly's since 1927 this traditional local pub on the Clontarf coast was established in 1845 by James Mooney of the Mooney pub empire. It is home to the Sportsman Bar and the Roaring Bull lounge upstairs which is now used by the Viking Theatre @The Sheds. The name refers to the sheds used by fisherman in past times to dry their fish. There is regular entertainment.

_ _/_ _/20_ _

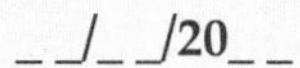

Cusack's

145 North Strand Road, Dublin 3, (1) 874 1417
Nautical memorabilia, including model ships in glass cases decorate this traditional local pub. There is a large selection of whiskeys behind the bar (147 different bottles on my latest visit). The locals enjoy having a singalong at any time. Matt Talbot reputedly drank his last pint here. Around 1965, Richard Burton visited the pub when he was filming *The Spy Who Came in From the Cold* in the neighbourhood. He was accompanied by his then wife, Elizabeth Taylor. She needed to use a toilet but there was no Ladies in the pub so she used the Gents instead, which the locals guarded. Richard bought drinks for all present. Every Christmas the bar is decorated for the festival with a fabulous display of model fairgrounds with moving carousels and attractions.

_ _/_ _/20_ _

Dollymount House

366 Clontarf Road, Dollymount, Dublin 3
A traditional local pub, currently closed.

_ _/_ _/20_ _

Duignan's The Beachcomber

179 Howth Road, Killester Village, Dublin 3
(1) 833 2673
A traditional local pub, refurbished in 2008. Food is served every day and there is occasional entertainment.

_ _/_ _/20_ _

Gaffney & Son

5–6 Fairview, Dublin 3
(1) 833 9803
A traditional Irish sports bar, generally considered to be one of the best pubs in North Dublin. It was established in the early 1700s and has traded as Gaffney's since circa 1914. There is a notice in the bar: 'Everybody who passes through these doors brings happiness, some by entering, some by leaving.' The pub's smoking garden is found, strangely enough, by going through the door marked 'Ladies'. There is occasional entertainment.

_ _/_ _/20_ _

Gilbert & Wright Hollybrook

Hollybrook Park, Clontarf, Dublin 3, (1) 833 8899
hollybrook@gilbertandwright.ie, www.gilbertandwright.ie
A bar and restaurant, opened in 2010. The restaurant is called Downstairs. The bar has a 1970s-theme with lots of sofas and memorabilia, including a wall of old televisions. The candlelit room and the 70s music in the background add to the atmosphere. Food is served every day and there is regular entertainment. At one time, The Hollybrook Hotel (known locally as Fawlty Towers) occupied this site. It housed Bram Stoker's Bar. Stoker, the author of *Dracula,* lived in Clontarf in the late 19th century. The hotel was demolished and rebuilt as the Parlour Bar, which later became Brook's Bar.

_ _/_ _/20_ _

Grainger's of Marino

Malahide Road, Marino, Dublin 3
(1) 833 2794
Previously called Gallagher's and The White House, this traditional local pub was established in 1945. Food is served every day and there is regular entertainment.

_ _/_ _/20_ _

Kavanagh's Marino House

16 Malahide Road, Marino, Dublin 3
(1) 833 2786
Many years ago this family-run traditional local pub was called J. Maguire's. There is a framed photo in the bar of a swinging sign outside the pub saying 'J. Maguire, late of the Stag's Head'. The pub is a good place for sports. It was refurbished in 2009 and serves food from Monday to Saturday.

_ _/_ _/20_ _

Knights Bar Clontarf Castle Hotel

Clontarf Castle Hotel, Castle Avenue, Clontarf, Dublin 3
(1) 833 2321
info@clontarfcastle.ie
www.clontarfcastle.ie
The bar of Clontarf Castle Hotel. The castle was built by Hugh de Lacy in 1172, as part of an inner circle of defence sites protecting Dublin. It has had many different owners over the centuries, eventually being converted to a cabaret venue and hotel in the 1960s. It has since been upgraded and refurbished, keeping many of its original features. Food is served every day and there is regular entertainment. The hotel is also home to the Indigo Lounge and the Fahrenheit Grill.

_ _/_ _/20_ _

Meagher's

283 Richmond Road, Ballybough, Dublin 3
(1) 837 1075
A traditional local pub with strong GAA support. In my younger days it was known as The Log Cabin and was run by the well-remembered Granny Meagher, 'the lady with the handbag'. Lunch is served every day except Saturday and there is occasional entertainment.

_ _/_ _/20_ _

Parnell Park House

Malahide Road, Donnycarney, Dublin 3
Previously called The Donnycarney House, Miller's and The Refuge. This pub is currently closed.

_ _/_ _/20_ _

Grainger's Pebble Beach

18 Conquer Hill Road, Clontarf, Dublin 3, (1) 833 2762
Graingers' Pebble Beach is a traditional pub, established in 1951, situated just behind Clontarf bus garage, locally known as The Pebbler. It was previously called The Vernon and gained its present name when a former proprietor, Mr Kinsella, visited the Pebble Beach Golf Links in California and renamed the pub when he returned home. Food is served every day. There is occasional entertainment.

_ _/_ _/20_ _

The Players Lounge

47 Fairview Strand, Fairview, Dublin 3
A traditional local sports bar 'run by sports people for sports people'. It was previously called Kelly's The Fairview Inn, and Murphy's. This pub is currently closed.

_ _/_ _/20_ _

The Ref Pub

70 Ballybough Road, Ballybough, Dublin 3
A traditional local pub near Croke Park, with regular entertainment. It was previously called Tom Clarke's, Collin's, The Blind Ref and most recently Molly's, after the proprietor's grandmother.

_ _/_ _/20_ _

Seabank House (Dillon's)

123 East Wall Road, East Wall, Dublin 3
(1) 856 0095
dillonspubs.info@gmail.com
www.dillonspubs.info
A traditional local pub, built on the site where The Wharf Tavern once stood. Food is served every day.

_ _/_ _/20_ _

The Sideline Bar

The Croke Park Hotel, Jones's Road, Dublin 3
(1) 871 4444
crokepark@doylecollection.com
www.doylecollection.com
Modern, stylish hotel bar and bistro, opposite Croke Park.

_ _/_ _/20_ _

Smyth's Fairview Bar

12 Fairview, Dublin 3
(1) 833 2767
info@smythsfairview.com
www.smythsfairview.com
A traditional local sports bar, licensed circa 1800. It also hosts The Barony Lounge and The Park Lounge. It was called The Grafton House around 1850, and was also previously called Cole's, but has traded as Smyth's since 1989. Food is served every day and there is regular entertainment.

_ _/_ _/20_ _

The Yacht

73 Clontarf Road, Clontarf, Dublin 3
(1) 833 6364
afcy@hotmail.com
A traditional local pub, completely refurbished in 2009. Food is served every day. Its previous name was Tobin's. It is my local pub when I am in Dublin. The staff are OK.

_ _/_ _/20_ _

The Ardlea Inn

11 Maryfield Avenue, Artane, Dublin 5
(1) 847 3997
A traditional local pub established in 1960 and known as 'The A-One'. Food is served on Saturdays and there is regular entertainment.

_ _/_ _/20_ _

The Artane House

Butterly Business Park, Kilmore Road, Artane, Dublin 5
(1) 704 7605
A traditional local pub, recently enhanced by a pool and snooker area. The pub was previously called Skelly's. Food is served every day and there is occasional entertainment.

_ _/_ _/20_ _

The Cedar Lounge

1 St Assam's Road, Raheny, Dublin 5
(1) 831 3738
A traditional local pub, known locally as The Cedars. It was used in filming scenes from the film *The Snapper*. There is regular entertainment.

_ _/_ _/20_ _

The Concorde

Edenmore Avenue, Edenmore, Dublin 5
(1) 847 8638
A traditional local pub with regular entertainment. It was established in 1979.

_ _/_ _/20_ _

Edenmore House

Edenmore Avenue, Raheny, Dublin 5, (1) 847 8408
A traditional local pub, with occasional entertainment, previously called Eugene's and The Satellite.

_ _/_ _/20_ _

The Foxhound Inn

Greendale Shopping Centre, Greendale Road, Dublin 5
(1) 839 1732
A traditional local pub, with regular entertainment. It was featured in the film *The Van*.

_ _/_ _/20_ _

The Goblet (McGovern's)

Malahide Road, Artane, Dublin 5
(1) 832 7311
A traditional local bar, lounge and restaurant. The bar is very much into sport and there are many GAA photos on the walls, including some of the local Artane Boys' Band in Croke Park. The pub has traded as Jim McGovern's since 1970. Food is served and there is regular entertainment.

_ _/_ _/20_ _

The Horse & Hound

44 Brookwood Rise, Artane, Dublin 5
A traditional local pub, previously called The Brookwood Inn. There is regular entertainment.

_ _/_ _/20_ _

The Inn

Main Street, Raheny, Dublin 5
(1) 831 4594
A traditional local pub with regular entertainment.

_ _/_ _/20_ _

Kyle's The Eastland House

Coolock Village, Coolock, Dublin 5
(1) 848 1972
A traditional local pub, with regular entertainment. It serves a light snack menu on weekdays.

_ _/_ _/20_ _

Liz Delaney's

Oscar Traynor Road, Coolock, Dublin 5
(1) 847 4282
lizdelaneys@eircom.net
This traditional pub located in the Northside Shopping Centre was established in the early 1970s. The premises also houses Dusk Club, formerly called Club Humuntra. The pub itself was once called The Black Sheep and is still referred to as The Blacker. There is regular entertainment.

_ _/_ _/20_ _

Madigan's of Kilbarrack

Grange Park Walk, Kilbarrack, Dublin 5
(1) 848 3575
www.madigan.ie
A traditional local pub with regular entertainment, located in Kilbarrack Shopping Centre. This pub was established in 1971.

_ _/_ _/20_ _

The Ramble Inn

145 Killester Avenue, Killester, Dublin 5,
(1) 831 3005
rambleinn@gmail.com
A traditional local pub, previously called Moran's.

_ _/_ _/20_ _

The Station House

Station Road, Raheny, Dublin 5
(1) 831 3772
stationhouseraheny@eircom.net
The interior of this traditional local pub is made from timber beams and posts. The lounge has a higher ceiling than the bar's and is more spacious. It also has an impressive brick fireplace and chimney in the centre of the room. This pub was previously called The Manhattan. Food is served every day and there is regular entertainment.

_ _/_ _/20_ _

The Roundabout

2 Ardcollum Avenue, Artane, Dublin 5
(1) 847 5002
A traditional local pub with regular entertainment.

_ _/_ _/20_ _

Sheaf O' Wheat (Grainger's)

Coolock Village, Dublin 5, (1) 848 0044
Grainger's Sheaf O'Wheat, also home to the Mill Lounge, is a traditional local pub, previously called Taylor's. A light snack menu is served on weekdays. There is regular entertainment.

_ _/_ _/20_ _

The Watermill

413 Howth Road, Raheny, Dublin 5
(1) 831 9574
A traditional local pub, also home to The Steakhouse Restaurant. Scenes from the film *The Snapper* were filmed here. The pub's previous name was The Green Dolphin. Food is served every day and there is regular entertainment.

_ _/_ _/20_ _

The Belfry

Stoneybatter, Dublin 7
A traditional local pub, currently closed.

_ _/_ _/20_ _

The Bohemian House (McGeough's)

66 North Circular Road, Phibsborough, Dublin 7, (1) 830 5505
McGeough's Bohemian House is a traditional local Victorian pub, previously called Geoghegan's, Mooney's Bohemian House, and John Doyle's. At one time this pub was linked to Doyle's pub on the opposite corner by their cellars under the road. McGeough's is also called The Bow Bar. Since taking over this pub in 1987, McGeoughs have done a great deal of restoration work on it, including taking the marble tiles off the external brickwork and removing the false ceiling to reveal the original Victorian ceiling. This pub was established in 1887 and rebuilt in 1906 after a fire. It is situated near Bohemian Football Club. Food is served every day and there is regular entertainment.

_ _/_ _/20_ _

The Berkeley

1 Mountjoy Street, Dublin 7
(1) 830 0372
Situated close to the Mater Hospital on the edge of the city centre this traditional local pub was established circa 1760.

_ _/_ _/20_ _

The Breffni Inn (Peacock's)

27–29 Ashtown Grove, off Navan Road, Cabra, Dublin 7
(1) 838 7303
Peacock's Breffni Inn is a traditional local pub situated just off the Navan Road, previously known as Kiernan's. A light snack menu is served and there is regular entertainment.

_ _/_ _/20_ _

The Cabra House

62 Faussagh Avenue, Cabra, Dublin 7
McGrath's Cabra House, a traditional local pub, was established in 1963. It was previously called Paddy Belton's and The Oasis.

_ _/_ _/20_ _

The Capel

1 Little Britain Street, Dublin 7
A local traditional early house situated near Dublin City Council's fruit and vegetable market. It was previously called Cameo, The Claddagh Ring, Culhane's of Green Street and The Green Bar. There is occasional entertainment.

_ _/_ _/20_ _

The Chancery Inn

Inns Quay, Dublin 7
(1) 677 0420
Established in the early 1800s this traditional city-centre early house, was previously called The Office Inn and O'Reilly Brothers. Food is served every day and there is occasional entertainment.

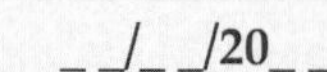

_ _/_ _/20_ _

Clarke's City Arms

55 Prussia Street, Dublin 7
(1) 868 1818
A traditional local pub with occasional entertainment.

_ _/_ _/20_ _

The Cobblestone

77 North King Street, Smithfield Square, Dublin 7
(1) 872 1799
www.cobblestonepub.ie
A traditional Irish music bar and venue with music every night. The pub was previously called Mulligan's.

_ _/_ _/20_ _

Cumiskey's

Blackhorse Avenue, Phoenix Park, Dublin 7
(1) 838 1609
afcy@hotmail.com
Previously called The Elm Grove Inn and The Turnstile this traditional local pub near the Phoenix Park was established in 1896. It houses The Rising Phoenix Restaurant on the first floor. A section of the pub is called Ned's Bar. Food is served every day.

_ _/_ _/20_ _

Cumiskey's

41 Upper Dominick Street, Phibsborough, Dublin 7
A traditional local pub established circa 1850. Food is served every day.

_ _/_ _/20_ _

Delaney's

83 North King St, Smithfield, Dublin 7
(1) 873 0824
A traditional local early house on the edge of Smithfield Square.
A light snack menu is served and there is regular entertainment.

_ _/_ _/20_ _

Dice Bar

79 Queen St, Smithfield, Dublin 7
(1) 633 3936
There has been a pub on this site since 1770. Dice Bar was previously called Mrs Loughman's, and is now a New York style music bar, open from 4 pm every day. DJs play music here regularly.

_ _/_ _/20_ _

Downey's Bar & Lounge

89 New Cabra Road, Cabra, Dublin 7
(1) 868 0605
Gerard Downey's traditional local pub was established in 1963.

_ _/_ _/20_ _

John Doyle's

160 Phibsborough Road, Phibsborough, Dublin 7, (1) 830 1441
Commonly known as Doyle's Corner because at one time two pubs both named Doyle's traded on opposite corners. This traditional local pub with entertainment has traded as Doyle's since around 1904. McGeough's pub on the opposite side of the road, The Bohemian House, was also previously called Doyle's (referring to the same family), and the two pubs were linked by a cellar under the road. In the early 1900s the pub was called Thomas Dunphy's. It is mentioned in James Joyce's *Ulysses* as Dunphy's Corner. The pub was also named Arthur Conan Doyle's at one time.

_ _/_ _/20_ _

Fibbers Rock Bar

27 Upper Ormond Quay, Dublin 7
manager@fibbermagees.ie, www.fibbermagees.ie
A sister pub to Fibber Magee's in Parnell Street, this bar and hard rock venue opened in 2010. Its previous names were The Blue Goose, Company, Elegance, The Four Courts Bar, The Office and Inn On The Liffey. A neighbouring B&B was called Out on the Liffey.

_ _/_ _/20_ _

Dec Gallagher's

15 Upper Dominic Street, Dublin 7
This traditional local pub is a good place for sport. It was established in the late 1800s and was previously called Flanagan's.

_ _/_ _/20_ _

Generator

Generator Hostel, Smithfield, Dublin 7, (1) 901 0222
www.generatorhostels.com
This hostel bar is generally only used by hostel residents (I was told this will change soon). Next door is the Smithfield Chimney Viewing Tower, also known as Chief O'Neill's Chimney. Built in 1895, the chimney was originally used to distil the famous Jameson Whiskey. This establishment was previously called The Park Inn Hotel Bar and Chief O'Neill's Bar.

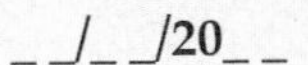

_ _/_ _/20_ _

The Glimmer Man

14–15 Manor Street, Stoneybatter, Dublin 7
(1) 677 9781
www.theglimmer.com
Named after the inspectors who used to call to houses to check on gas usage during the Emergency (as the Second World War was known in Ireland) when gas was rationed to an hour in the morning and an hour in the evening. This traditional local pub was established around 1880 and was previously called Paddy Carr's and Lyster's. Join the locals for Sing-a-Long Sunday.

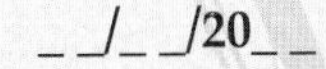

_ _/_ _/20_ _

The Grange Inn

19 Lower Grangegorman Road, Dublin 7
Tucked away behind the old Grangegorman Hospital this traditional local pub was previously called O'Dowd's.

_ _/_ _/20_ _

Hacienda Market Bar

East Arran Street, Dublin 7
A private members' bar.

_ _/_ _/20_ _

The Halfway House

Ashtown, Navan Road, Dublin 7
(1) 838 3218
Con Treacy's Halfway House is a traditional local pub established around 1930. It was previously known as Kelly's. Food is served every day and there is occasional entertainment. The pub is also home to The Mulberry Restaurant.

_ _/_ _/20_ _

John J. Hanlon

189 North Circular Road, Dublin 7
(1) 810 2054
www.hanlons.ie
Known as Hanlon's Corner because it has entrances on three different roads, this traditional Victorian local bar and venue was established in 1886. Food is served every day and there is regular entertainment.

_ _/_ _/20_ _

The Hole In The Wall

Blackhorse Avenue, Dublin 7, (1) 838 9491
carolineholeinthewall@gmail.com
McCaffren's Hole in the Wall is a traditional local pub established in 1681 and built on part of the outer wall of the Phoenix Park. The pub's name comes from an old tradition of dispensing drinks to the army garrison stationed in the Phoenix Park through a hole in the wall. It was once Europe's longest bar. However, some time ago an off-licence was constructed in the centre of the house, cutting the bar length. The pub has open turf fires in winter. Food is served every day and there is regular entertainment.

_ _/_ _/20_ _

Homestead

Quarry Road, Cabra, Dublin 7
(1) 868 0423
Kiernan's Homestead Bar is a traditional local pub with regular entertainment. It was established in 1947.

_ _/_ _/20_ _

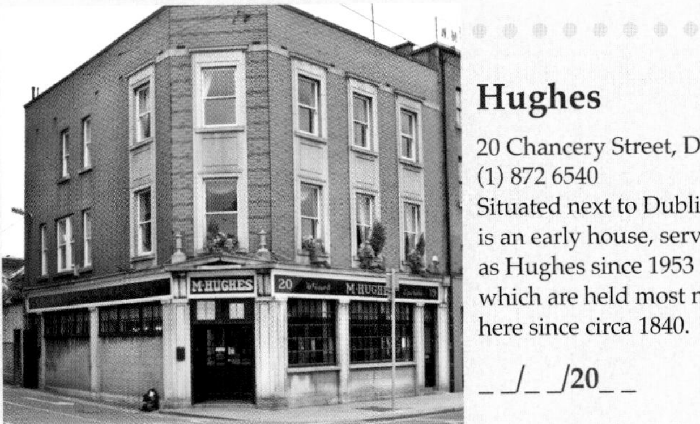

Hughes

20 Chancery Street, Dublin 7
(1) 872 6540
Situated next to Dublin City Council's fruit and vegetable market this is an early house, serving both locals and market traders. It has traded as Hughes since 1953 and is famous for its traditional music sessions, which are held most nights. Food is served every day. A pub has stood here since circa 1840.

_ _/_ _/20_ _

The Hut (Mohan's)

159 Phibsborough Road, Phibsborough, Dublin 7
(1) 830 2238
Mohan's The Hut is a traditional local Victorian pub, with great timberwork and paintings throughout the long, narrow, tall building. The pub was established in the 1830s. It was previously called Maher's. Lunch is served on weekdays.

_ _/_ _/20_ _

Hyne's Bar

Prussia Street, Dublin 7
(1) 868 4395
A traditional local pub with regular entertainment. Its previous names were The Banner, Brennan's and O'Reilly's.

_ _/_ _/20_ _

Kavanagh's of Aughrim Street

1 Aughrim Street, Dublin 7, (1) 838 6215
kavanaghsd7@ireland.com
Established in 1777 and rebuilt in 1901 this traditional local pub has traded under this name since 1988. Scenes from the films *When Brendan Met Trudy* and *Dear Sarah* were filmed here. Food is served on weekdays and there is occasional entertainment. The current proprietor's name, Peacock, is etched in the glass in one of the windows.

_ _/_ _/20_ _

The Last Waterhole

199 North King Street, Dublin 7
A traditional local pub with regular entertainment. It was previously called The Four Seasons and then traded as an off-licence for a few years. It reopened as O'Byrnes Beverage House in 2010, the name taken from the GAA O'Byrne Cup, and later traded as Rúta.

_ _/_ _/20_ _

The Legal Eagle

Chancery Place, Dublin 7
(1) 873 5031
legaleagle@gmail.com
www.thebar.ie
Being opposite the Four Courts, this traditional city-centre pub is a favourite hangout for lawyers. It was previously called The Tilted Wig and is also known as The Bar. There is a second entrance on West Charles Street. Food is served on weekdays and there is regular entertainment.

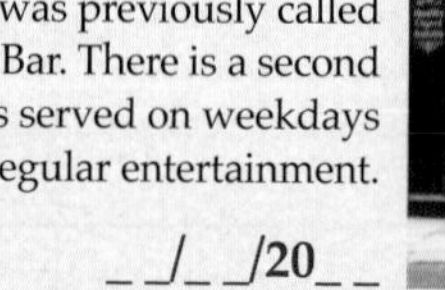

_ _/_ _/20_ _

Noel Lennon's

40 Watling Street, Victoria Quay, Dublin 7
A traditional local pub situated near Guinness's Brewery. It is currently closed. Passing by the pub in early 2012, I saw it had new signage which bore the name The Napper Tandy and then discovered that it was being used a location for a new Irish film. Napper Tandy is mentioned in 'The Wearing of the Green', an old Irish song. Whenever I mention the name, my mother Kathleen breaks into song, 'I met with Napper Tandy, and he took me by the hand, saying how is poor old Ireland, and what way does she stand?'

_ _/_ _/20_ _

Mac Aodha's

Ellis Quay, Dublin 7
This traditional pub is currently closed. It was previously called The Croppy Acre.

_ _/_ _/20_ _

H. Mathews

17 Benburb Street, Dublin 7
(1) 672 8899
A traditional local pub with regular entertainment near the city centre. It was previously called Harry Matthews.

_ _/_ _/20_ _

Matt's of Cabra

2a Faussagh Avenue, Cabra, Dublin 7
(1) 868 0145
A traditional local pub with regular entertainment. It was previously called The Faussagh House, Lloyd's, Matt Whelan's and most recently The Sixpenny Bit. It was established in 1946.

_ _/_ _/20_ _

McGettigan's

78 Queen Street, Dublin 7
(1) 872 1905
A small atmospheric pub on the edge of the city centre, with lots of old pictures on the walls. It has traded as McGettigan's since 1964 and has regular entertainment. There has been a pub here since around 1770.

_ _/_ _/20_ _

McGowan's of Phibsborough

17–18 Phibsborough Road, Phibsborough, Dublin 7
(1) 830 6606
info@mcgowans.ie
www.mcgowans.ie
A traditional local pub and club, originally established in 1860. 'The Pub With The Buzz.' There are many interesting items on display throughout the pub, including an old telephone box and over 200 American car number plates. It was previously called The Broadstone Inn. Food is served every day and there is entertainment.

_ _/_ _/20_ _

E. McGrath's

30–32 Fassaugh Avenue, Cabra, Dublin 7
(1) 868 0079
A traditional local pub established around 1940. This pub was previously called Kennedy's and The Local. A light snack menu is served.

_ _/_ _/20_ _

The Mill

199 Phibsborough Road, Phibsborough, Dublin 7
themillspiritsltd@gmail.com
A traditional local pub, reopened in 2012. At one time it was run by Kate Gilligan, better known as Widow Reilly. She weighed 20 stone and was the bouncer of her own pub. She also ran a matchmaking service, arranging suitable marriages for a fee. The pub was previously called The Mill and the Red Windmill. Food is served every day and there is occasional entertainment.

_ _/_ _/20_ _

L. Mulligan, Grocer

18 Manor Street, Stoneybatter, Dublin 7
(1) 670 9889
hello@mulligangrocer.com
www.lmulligangrocer.com
Now a well-regarded eating and drinking emporium this pub was first established as a bar and grocer in 1792. It changed hands in 2010 and boasts of having over 100 different whiskeys and 100 beers in stock. It is on The Irish Whiskey Trail.

_ _/_ _/20_ _

Paddy Murphy's

32 Upper Dominick Street, Dublin 7
This traditional local pub was previously called The Phoenix. It was rebuilt in 1997. There is regular entertainment.

_ _/_ _/20_ _

The Museum Rest

5 Benburb Street, Dublin 7
Currently closed due to fire this traditional local pub is on the edge of the city near the National Museum of Decorative Arts and History (Collins Barracks). It was previously called The Breffni Inn and The Regal Bar.

_ _/_ _/20_ _

Number 6 Smithfield

Unit 6a/b, Smithfield Square, Smithfield, Dublin 7
A modern café bar which first opened in 2008 under the name Thomas Read Smithfield. In 2010 it opened under the name Number 6 Smithfield but is currently closed.

_ _/_ _/20_ _

Phibsborough House

Phibsborough Road, Phibsborough,
Dublin 7, (1) 830 3372
Clarke's Phibsborough House is a traditional local pub, previously called John Davy. It was established in 1889. Food is served every day and there is occasional entertainment

_ _/_ _/20_ _

Eamonn Rea's

25 Parkgate Street, Dublin 7
A traditional local pub near Phoenix Park and Heuston Station. It was previously called The Sportsman's Rest. Food is served on weekdays.

_ _/_ _/20_ _

The Richmond

119 Church Street, Dublin 7
(1) 874 6412
A traditional local pub with regular entertainment. It was previously called John Tavey's.

_ _/_ _/20_ _

Frank Ryan's

5 Queen Street, Smithfield, Dublin 7
(1) 872 5204
www.frankryans.com
A traditional local pub on the edge of the city centre. There is another entrance on a side street off Smithfield Square called Coke Lane. A light snack menu is served and there is regular entertainment.

_ _/_ _/20_ _

Sin É

14 Upper Ormond Quay, Dublin 7
(1) 547 0530
Sin É means 'That's it'. This is a city-centre pub with a difference, 'Walk In, Dance Out'. A light snack menu is served and there is regular entertainment.

_ _/_ _/20_ _

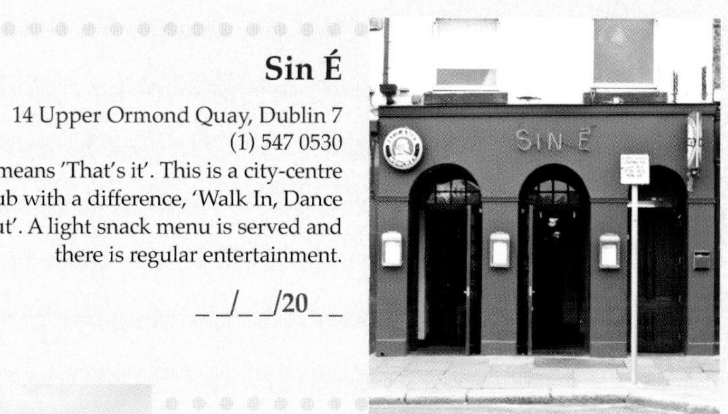

Smith's of Phibsborough

114–115 Phibsborough Road, Crossguns Bridge, Phibsborough, Dublin 7
(1) 860 3227
smithsofphibsboro@gmail.com
www.thesmithgroup.ie
A traditional local pub near Crossguns Bridge, only five minutes' walk to Croke Park along the Royal Canal. The pub was previously called Bush's and Mick O'Mahoney's. Food is served every day and there is regular entertainment.

_ _/_ _/20_ _

Stir Café Bar

The Maldron Hotel, Smithfield, Dublin 7
(1) 485 0900
info.smithfield@maldronhotels.com
www.maldronhotels.com
Café bar of The Maldron Hotel. Previously the hotel was called The Comfort Inn Dublin.

_ _/_ _/20_ _

The Tap

44 North King Street, Dublin 7
A traditional local pub. It was established in 1776. Food is served every day and there is regular entertainment.

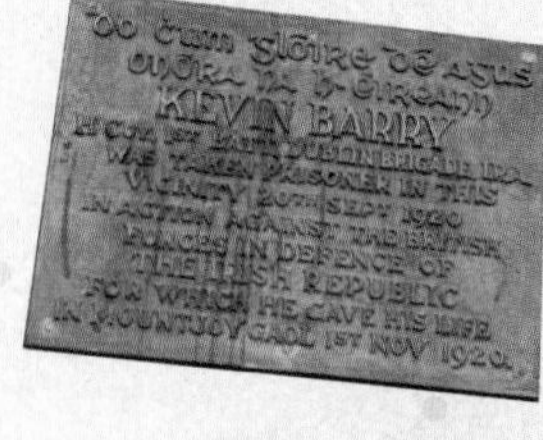

_ _/_ _/20_ _

Tommy O'Gara's

Manor Street, Stoneybatter, Dublin 7
(1) 677 8178
I am told that this traditional local pub, known locally as Tommy's, is the oldest pub in Stoneybatter. It was established in 1764.

_ _/_ _/20_ _

The Muddy Boot

Manor Street, Stoneybatter, Dublin 7
This establishment is currently closed as a pub and is trading as a convenience store. It was previously called McKenan's and Stoney's Bar. A pub stood here from 1905.

_ _/_ _/20_ _

Voodoo

Arran Quay, Dublin 7
A bar and venue situated close to the city centre. It is currently trading as a casino.

_ _/_ _/20_ _

Liam Walsh's The Furry Glen

36 Parkgate Street, Dublin 7
A traditional local pub located near the Phoenix Park and Heuston Station. It was previously called Kelly's and Quinlan's. This pub is currently closed.

_ _/_ _/20_ _

J. Walsh's

6 Stoneybatter, Manor Street, Dublin 7
A traditional pub, with a great snug, full of character and characters, situated near the city centre.

_ _/_ _/20_ _

The Addison Lodge

Botanic Road, Glasnevin, Dublin 9
(1) 837 3534
addison@eircom.net
A traditional local bar located close to the Botanic Gardens. At one time it offered accommodation. Food is served every day and there is entertainment.

_ _/_ _/20_ _

The Appian Bar

The Regency Hotel, Swords Road, Whitehall, Dublin 9
(1) 837 3544
regency@regencyhotel.com
www.regencyhotels.com
Hotel bar of The Regency Hotel which is also home to The Shanard Restaurant. The hotel was previously called The Crofton Airport Hotel.

_ _/_ _/20_ _

The Beaumont House

1 Shantalla Road, Beaumont, Dublin 9
(1) 837 1008
beaumonthouse@eircom.net
A traditional local pub near Beaumont Hospital, previously called Belton's and The Rendezvous. The premises was built in the grounds of the Arthur Guinness estate. The pub was established in 1953. Food is served every day and there is regular entertainment.

_ _/_ _/20_ _

The Botanic

22–26 Botanic Road and Prospect Avenue, Glasnevin, Dublin 9
(01) 8500503
Previously called Fitzsimon's Botanic House, this traditional local pub is housed in a building that dates back to 1913. Food is served every day and there is regular entertainment.

_ _/_ _/20_ _

The Cat and Cage

74 Upper Drumcondra Road, Drumcondra, Dublin 9
(1) 857 3809
www.catandcage.ie
One of Dublin's oldest surviving coach houses, this traditional local pub was established in 1689. Food is served every day and there is regular entertainment.

_ _/_ _/20_ _

Cinnabar

Crowne Plaza Hotel, Northwood Park Santry Demesne, Santry, Dublin 9
(1) 862 8888
info@crowneplazadublin.ie
www.cpdublin-airport.com
Hotel bar of the Crowne Plaza Hotel. Food is served in the bar every day. The hotel, which opened in 2003, is situated in Northwood Park which covers 85 acres and includes a lake.

_ _/_ _/20_ _

The Comet

243–245 Swords Road, Santry, Dublin 9
(1) 842 4986
O'Mara's The Comet is a traditional local pub established in 1959. A light snack menu is served and there is regular entertainment.

_ _/_ _/20_ _

Fagan's

146 Lower Drumcondra Road, Drumcondra, Dublin 9
(1) 837 5309
afcy@hotmail.com
A traditional local pub, a good place for sport. It has been well extended over the years. This pub can lay claim to many famous customers, including former Taoiseach Bertie Ahern and actor Colm Meaney. President Bill Clinton once popped in to see his friend Bertie in 2000. The pub was established in 1907.

_ _/_ _/20_ _

The Goose Tavern

20 Sion Hill Road, Drumcondra, Dublin 9
(1) 836 8775
A traditional local pub with occasional entertainment. Its previous name was The Pilot.

_ _/_ _/20_ _

Hedigan's The Brian Boru

5 Prospect Road, Glasnevin, Dublin 9
(1) 830 4527
info@thebrianboru.ie
www.thebrianboru.ie
A traditional local pub which is on The Irish Whiskey Trail and is home to Dublin's literary writers' room. The entertainment on offer includes a theatre night on the last Thursday of the month and live music at the Loft Music Venue. The picture on the front of the pub is of the Irish King Brian Boru leading his army in the Battle of Clontarf in 1014. There has been a pub on this site since the early 1800s, and it has traded as Hedigan's since 1904. Food is served every day and there is occasional entertainment.

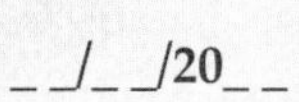
_ _/_ _/20_ _

Holiday Inn Express

Holiday Inn Express, Northwood Park, Santry Demesne, Dublin 9
(1) 862 8866
info@hiexpressdublin-airport.ie
www.hiexpressdublin-airport.ie
This hotel bar, which is mainly used by residents, is open from seven every evening. The hotel, which opened in 2003, is a sister hotel to The Crowne Plaza next door. It is situated in Northwood Park grounds, which covers 85 acres and includes a lake.

_ _/_ _/20_ _

The Ivy House (Carthy's)

114 Upper Drumcondra Road, Drumcondra, Dublin 9, (1) 837 5385
info@theivyhouse.ie, www.theivyhouse.ie
Patrick Carthy and Son The Ivy House is a contemporary bar and lounge, established in 1922, with highly varied entertainment: DJs; The Littlest Theatre, a theatre night; movie nights; and plenty more. This is also a good pub to watch sport. The bar has a large selection of whiskeys. Its entrance is through a street at the side of the pub. Food is served every day.

_ _/_ _/20_ _

Kavanagh's 'The Gravediggers'

1–2 Prospect Square, Phibsborough, Dublin 9
ciarankav@gmail.com
Known as The Gravediggers as well as Kavanagh's, this traditional local pub is situated next door to Glasnevin Cemetery. I am told that gravediggers used to put their shovels with the price of a pint on them through a hole in the wall. The drinks would be then placed on the shovels, taken back by the bearers and consumed! It is one of the few pubs where the patrons play throw rings, a game where players throw rings onto a board like a darts board which has hooks with numbers. This pub has been run by seven generations of the Kavanagh family since 1833. Food is served on weekdays.

_ _/_ _/20_ _

Kennedy's

132–134 Lower Drumcondra Road, Drumcondra, Dublin 9
(1) 837 1080
A traditional local pub previously called McPhilips. It is situated near Croke Park and has many old GAA pictures on display in the bar. A light snack menu is served.

_ _/_ _/20_ _

Kenny's The Kilmardinny Inn

73–83 Lorcan Avenue, Beaumont, Dublin 9
(1) 842 0238
A traditional local pub, known locally as The Killo. There is regular entertainment.

_ _/_ _/20_ _

Kitty Kiernan's

Collins Ave, Donnycarney, Dublin 9
(1) 831 5437
Named after Michael Collins' lover, this traditional local pub was previously called The Jolly Beggar Man. Before that it was called Paddy Belton's, after the developer of part of the surrounding area. I am told it was also called The Nineteen, in reference to the nearby Clontarf Golf Club. Food is served every day and there is regular entertainment.

_ _/_ _/20_ _

Patrick McGrath's

22 Lower Drumcondra Road, Drumcondra, Dublin 9
(1) 830 6004
A traditional local pub near Croke Park, dating back to 1938. It is also known as The Grattan House. A light snack menu is served on weekdays.

_ _/_ _/20_ _

Millmount House

Lower Drumcondra Road, Drumcondra, Dublin 9
(1) 837 1103
A traditional bar and club with regular entertainment. It is the prison officers' club and is also used by locals. It is referred to in Irish as Teach an Muileann—Mill House.

_ _/_ _/20_ _

The Porterhouse North

Crossguns Bridge, Phibsborough, Dublin 9
(1) 830 9884
www.porterhousebrewco.com
A large modern bar, housed within an Art Deco-style building. Food is served every day and there is regular entertainment.

_ _/_ _/20_ _

Quinn's

42–44 Lower Drumcondra Road, Drumcondra, Dublin 9
(1) 830 4973
www.quinnhotels.com
This traditional local pub near Croke Park has traded as Quinn's since 1987. It was previously called McGovern's and Cooks. There is regular entertainment.

_ _/_ _/20_ _

The Skylon Bar

The Dublin Skylon Hotel, Upper Drumcondra Road, Drumcondra, Dublin 9
(1) 844 3900
reservations@dublinskylonhotel.com
www.dublinskylonhotel.com
A traditional bar at the Dublin Skylon Hotel. Food is served every day and there is entertainment. The hotel also houses The Rendezvous Restaurant.

_ _/_ _/20_ _

Sunny Bank Bar and Lounge

Sunny Bank Hotel, 68–70 Botanic Avenue, Glasnevin, Dublin 9
(1) 830 6755
info@sunnybank.ie
www.sunnybank.ie
A hotel bar and lounge. Food is served every day and there is regular entertainment.

_ _/_ _/20_ _

The Swiss Cottage

Swords Road, Santry, Dublin 9
(1) 842 8096
A traditional local pub, once home to Chimes Nightclub. Food is served every day and there is regular entertainment.

_ _/_ _/20_ _

The Tolka House

Glasnevin Road, Glasnevin, Dublin 9
(1) 837 1082
Many years ago I worked as an apprentice barman in this traditional local pub for six months. The pub was established in 1873. Food is served every day and there is regular entertainment.

_ _/_ _/20_ _

The Viscount (O'Connell's)

89 Swords Road, Whitehall, Dublin 9
(1) 837 4492
S. O'Connell's Viscount is a traditional local pub. A section of the pub is called The Air Lounge. Food from OCs' restaurant upstairs is served every day and there is regular entertainment. The pub was established in 1948.

_ _/_ _/20_ _

An Cappagh Nua

Barry Road, Finglas, Dublin 11
This traditional local pub was previously called The Barry House, The Cappagh House and The Finglas Inn. When it was called the Barry House, it was managed by Tom and Catherine Nevin. Mrs Nevin became known as 'the Black Widow' because she was found guilty of murdering her husband.

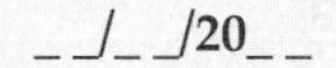
_ _/_ _/20_ _

Autobahn Roadhouse

73 Glasnevin Avenue, Glasnevin, Dublin 11
(1) 842 5201
afcy@hotmail.com
A traditional local pub established circa 1950. I am told they once had a restaurant upstairs which was renowned for having a circular bar. Food is served every day and there is regular entertainment.

_ _/_ _/20_ _

Bottom of the Hill (Gleeson's)

34 Main Street, Finglas, Dublin 11
(1) 834 8615
Established in 1641, this pub describes itself as 'An Inn of Heritage, Hospitality and Character'. Food is served on Sundays and bank holiday Mondays. There is regular entertainment.

_ _/_ _/20_ _

The Cardiff Inn

Cardiffsbridge Road, Finglas, Dublin 11
(1) 834 3317
A traditional local pub with regular entertainment, established in 1969.

_ _/_ _/20_ _

The Cremore House

21 Glasilawn Avenue, Glasnevin, Dublin 11
(1) 834 8016
Previously called The Glasilawn House this traditional local pub with regular entertainment was established circa 1950.

_ _/_ _/20_ _

The Deputy Mayor

Distribution Road, Finglas / Meakstown, Dublin 11
(1) 864 4053
A traditional local pub, established in 2006. Food is served every day and there is regular entertainment.

_ _/_ _/20_ _

The Drake Inn

Main Street, Finglas, Dublin 11
This pub which was established in 1823 is currently closed. At one time a pub called The Duck was situated near The Drake.

_ _/_ _/20_ _

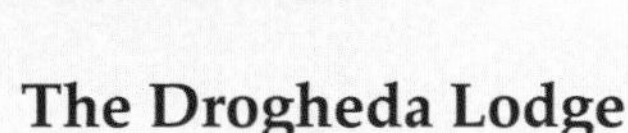

The Drogheda Lodge

66–67 Main Street, Finglas, Dublin 11, 01 8346061 / 01 8641895
info@droghedalodge.ie
Established in 1975 this traditional local pub with regular entertainment used to be The Drogheda Stores Grocer and was previously the Earl of Drogheda's hunting lodge. A house called Gofton Hall once stood on a site nearby. In 1994 a new section called The Full Shilling Pub was added at the rear. This section has many historical interesting items throughout, including a pony trap which was featured in the film *The Quiet Man*, and some old lanterns, two bearing the name The Haggard, and one with the name Watery Lane Station.

_ _/_ _/20_ _

The Fingal House

284 Glasnevin Avenue, Finglas, Dublin 11
(1) 836 1159
thefingalhouse@eircom.net
This traditional local pub, established in 1953, has regular entertainment and occasionally hosts line dancing nights. The staff say the upstairs level is haunted.

_ _/_ _/20_ _

Martin's

122 Ballygall Road, Finglas, Dublin 11
(1) 834 2183
A traditional local pub with regular entertainment.
This pub was previously called Kirwan's.

_ _/_ _/20_ _

Matt Weldon's The Slipper

125 Ballymun Road, Glasnevin, Dublin 11
(1) 857 0114
This traditional local pub, close to Dublin City University (DCU), was built in 1954 in a then rural setting. Over the years it has grown along with residential development in its surroundings. Sections of the pub are called The Albert Lounge and The College Lounge. Food is served every day and there is regular entertainment.

_ _/_ _/20_ _

Metzo Bar and Resturant

Travelodge Airport Hotel, Main Street, Ballymun, Dublin 11, (1) 852 4516
ballymundublinairport@travelodge.ie
www.travelodge.ie
Hotel bar of The Travelodge Airport Hotel Ballymun. Food is served every day.

_ _/_ _/20_ _

The Penthouse

Sillogue Road, Ballymun, Dublin 11
A traditional local pub situated in Ballymun Shopping Centre. It traded as an off-licence for the past few years, reverting to a pub in 2010. It was also home to Club Tonic. This pub is currrently closed.

_ _/_ _/20_ _

The Premier Bar

The Ardmore Hotel, Tolka Valley, Glasnevin/Finglas, Dublin 11
(1) 864 8300
reservations@ardmorehotel.com
www.ardmore-hotel.com
This hotel bar is named after The Premier Dairies which traded from a site near here. Food is served every day and there is regular entertainment. The hotel is located between Glasnevin and Finglas and also houses The Cream Restaurant.

_ _/_ _/20_ _

Quarry House

68 Ballygall Road East, Glasnevin, Dublin 11
(1) 836 2300
A traditional local pub with regular entertainment, established in 1968. There is a quote by Brendan Behan displayed in the pub: 'I once saw a sign, "Drink Canada Dry", so I've started.'

_ _/_ _/20_ _

The Shamrock Lodge

Seamus Ennis Road, Finglas, Dublin 11
(1) 864 5044
www.quinnhotels.com
A traditional local pub with regular entertainment. Food is served every day.

_ _/_ _/20_ _

The Towers

Ballymun Shopping Centre, Ballymun Road, Ballymun, Dublin 11
Built in the 1960s this traditional local pub with regular entertainment is situated in the Ballymun Shopping Centre.

_ _/_ _/20_ _

The Village Inn

Church Street, Finglas, Dublin 11
(1) 834 1180
A traditional local pub, previously called The Jolly Toper.
There is regular entertainment.

_ _/_ _/20_ _

The Willows

74 Willow Park Crescent, Glasnevin, Dublin 11
A traditional local pub. Food is served every day and there is occasional entertainment.

_ _/_ _/20_ _

The Donaghmede Inn

Donaghmede Shopping Centre, Grange Road,
Donaghmede, Dublin 13
(1) 847 4555
A traditional local pub, with regular entertainment, previously called Madigan's. Part of the pub is the Cellar Bar, which is mostly used as a function room.

_ _/_ _/20_ _

The Elphin

36 Baldoyle Road, Sutton, Dublin 13
(1) 832 2495
www.elphin.ie
A traditional local pub. It was renovated in 2007. 'It's as out of place as a snowman in the desert and yet it's exactly where it should be.' Food is served seven days a week.

_ _/_ _/20_ _

Grainger's Baldoyle House

12–13 Main Street, Baldoyle, Dublin 13
(1) 832 2323
Near the coast, this traditional local pub, with bed and breakfast accommodation, was established circa 1910 and has traded as Grainger's since 1979. Food is served every day and there is entertainment.

_ _/_ _/20_ _

Lynch's Bayside Inn

Bayside Square North, Bayside, Dublin 13
(1) 839 1329
Established in 1974 this large traditional pub has high ceilings showing timber roof beams.

_ _/_ _/20_ _

The Racecourse Inn

Grange Road, Baldoyle, Dublin 13
(1) 839 1816
A traditional local pub with regular entertainment.

_ _/_ _/20_ _

The Schooner Bar

The Marine Hotel, Greenfields Road, Sutton Cross, Dublin 13
(1) 839 0000
info@marinehotel.ie
www.marinehotel.ie
A traditional hotel bar situated in the Marine Hotel, Sutton which is also home to Hardy's Bar, The Meridian Bistro and The Galley Carvery. The hotel was established in 1897. The Schooner Bar has a view over Dublin's coast. It is the only bar in the village.

_ _/_ _/20_ _

The Bell

Main Street, Blanchardstown, Dublin 15, (1) 820 0158
info@thebellpub.ie, www.thebellpub.ie
A traditional local pub. It was previously called Davy and Phelan's Bar and a section of the pub still bears this name. Food is served every day and there is regular entertainment.

_ _/_ _/20_ _

Brady's The Castleknock Inn

Old Navan Road, Castleknock, Dublin 15
(1) 821 3445
A traditional local pub, previously called The Twin Oaks and trading as Brady's since 1998. Food is served every day.

_ _/_ _/20_ _

Brasserie 15

Ashleigh Centre, Main Street, Castleknock, Dublin 15
(1) 821 8580
brasserie15@gmail.com
www.brasserie15.com
A local bar with entertainment on Saturdays. It was previously called Barbican. Food is served every day in the bar. The brasserie is French style.

_ _/_ _/20_ _

The Brock Inn (Farrell's)

Ashbourne Road, The Ward/Corduff, Dublin 15
(1) 834 2216
Farrell's The Brock Inn is a traditional roadhouse and local pub very much into darts—many tournaments are held here. Food is served every day. The pub was previously called McGuinness's and The Red House. It was established in the early 1700s. I am told it has never been sold and instead was handed down to family, friends and staff over the centuries. Farrells also own a pitch and putt course which is beside the pub.

_ _/_ _/20_ _

The Canal Bar

73–74 Ashtown Village, Dublin 15
(1) 866 4970
canalbar.dublin@gmail.com
www.canalbar.ie www.geisha.ie
A traditional local pub established in 2011 and home to Geisha Asian Restaurant. It is situated along The Royal Canal at Lock 10, next to Ashtown railway station. Food is served every day and there is regular entertainment.

_ _/_ _/20_ _

Captain America's

Unit 410 Blanchardstown Retail Park 2, Blanchardstown, Dublin 15, (1) 826 2340
blanch@captainamericas.com
www.captainamericas.com
www.captainslive.com
Opened in 2010 this is an American-style bar, restaurant and music venue 'The Captain Live'. The restaurant has various pieces of music memorabilia on display. Captain America's was first established in Dublin in 1971.

_ _/_ _/20_ _

The Carpenter

Carpenterstown Road, Carpenterstown, Dublin 15
(1) 821 9440
A traditional local pub with entertainment on bank holidays. Food is served every day.

_ _/_ _/20_ _

The Clonsilla Inn

Weavers Road, Clonsilla, Dublin 15
(1) 821 3658
A traditional local pub, home to the Weavers Music Lounge, a well-known music venue. Dickie Rock, Bagatelle and Dublin City Ramblers have played here. There are cabinets throughout the lounge containing artifacts and old hardback books. Food is served every day.

_ _/_ _/20_ _

Fionn Uisce Bar

Castleknock Hotel and Country Club, Porterstown Road, Castleknock, Dublin 15
(1) 640 6300
events@chcc.ie
www.castleknockhotel.com
This hotel bar has great views of Castleknock golf course. Food is served every day. The hotel also houses The Lime Tree Bar, The Park Restaurant and The Brasserie. It was established in 2005.

_ _/_ _/20_ _

Dolly Heffernan's

Ballycoolin, Blanchardstown, Dublin 15
A traditional pub, with a thatched roof, currently closed.

_ _/_ _/20_ _

The Greyhound Inn

Main Street, Blanchardstown, Dublin 15
(1) 811 1125
A traditional local pub, established circa 1965. Food is served every day and there is regular entertainment.

_ _/_ _/20_ _

The Hourglass Bar

The Carlton Hotel, Church Road, Tyrellstown, Dublin 15
(1) 827 5600
reservationsblanchardstown@carlton.ie
www.carlton.ie
Food is served in this hotel bar every day. The hotel opened in 2006 as The Park Plaza Hotel Tyrellstown and changed its name to The Carlton Hotel in 2011. It also houses The Time Restaurant.

_ _/_ _/20_ _

Kavanagh's of Castleknock

Laurel Lodge Road, Castleknock, Dublin 15
(1) 820 5916
A traditional local pub with entertainment on bank holiday Saturdays. It was previously called The Laurel Lodge.

_ _/_ _/20_ _

Tom Meagher's Hartstown House

Hartstown, Clonsilla, Dublin 15
(1) 820 6696
A traditional local pub with regular entertainment. The pub was established in 1984. A light snack menu is served.

_ _/_ _/20_ _

Michael Grace & Sons The Brookwood Inn

Corduff Shopping Centre, Blackcourt Road, Corduff, Dublin 15, (1) 822 3286
This traditional local pub which was established circa 1980 was previously called The Corduff Inn. Brookwood was the name of the owner's previous pub. There is occasional entertainment.

_ _/_ _/20_ _

Myo's

Main Street, Castleknock, Dublin 15
(1) 821 0529
A traditional village pub very much into sport. It has a great gallery of caricature paintings of past golf captains on display. Food is served seven days a week.

_ _/_ _/20_ _

Jack O'Neill's

Unit 1, Block C, Tyrellstown Town Centre, Dublin 15
(1) 827 4039
manager@jackoneills.com, www.jackoneills.com
A traditional local bar and bistro, established in 2004. It was previously called Cruiser's Bar and Grill and The Thirsty Bull. It has traded as O'Neill's since 2011. Food is served every day and there is regular entertainment.

_ _/_ _/20_ _

Paidi Og's

Main Street, Mulhuddart, Dublin 15
(1) 810 3111
A traditional local pub and club, previously called Bertie Donnelly's, The Lodge and The Shanty. Status Nightclub and music venue opens on Saturdays. Food is served every day and there is regular entertainment.

_ _/_ _/20_ _

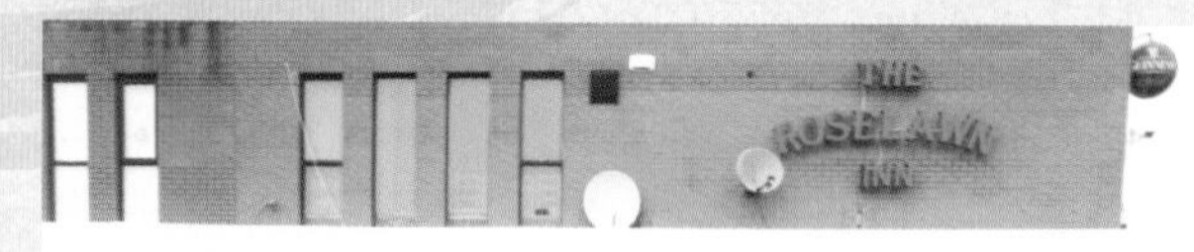

The Roselawn Inn

Roselawn Shopping Centre, Roselawn Road, Castleknock, Dublin 15, (1) 821 7443
Locals call this traditional local pub The Rosie. It was previously called Madigan's and was first established in 1977. The bar is called The Par 3 Bar. Food is served Monday to Saturday and there is regular entertainment.

_ _/_ _/20_ _

Salmon's Public House

Mountview Shopping Centre, Mountview Road, Blanchardstown, Dublin 15
(1) 821 9551
A traditional local pub and music venue, established in 2002. A pub called The Mountview once stood near here; it was demolished before Salmon's opened. Food is served every day and there is regular entertainment.

_ _/_ _/20_ _

The Sanctuary Bar

The Crowne Plaza Hotel, The Blanchardstown Centre, Blanchardstown, Dublin 15, (1) 897 7777
info@crowneplazadublinwest.ie
www.dublinwest.crowneplaza.com
Hotel bar of the Crowne Plaza Hotel. Food is served every day in the bar. The hotel, which opened in 2008, also houses The Forchetta Italian Restaurant.

_ _/_ _/20_ _

TGI Friday's

Westland Retail Park, Blanchardstown, Dublin 15, (1) 822 5990
blanch@fridays.ie, www.fridays.ie
A branch of the American restaurant and bar chain. 'In here, it's always Friday'. The interior is filled with interesting items which include various kinds of automobile, musical and sports memorabilia.

_ _/_ _/20_ _

The Twelfth Lock

The Twelfth Lock Hotel, Castleknock Marina, Castleknock, Dublin 15, (1) 860 7400
info@twelfthlock.com, www.twelfthlock.com
A modern bar in the Twelfth Lock Hotel which is situated along the Royal Canal. The hotel also houses The Dam Square Restaurant. This boutique hotel's style was inspired by the hotels, cafés and bars of Paris and Amsterdam. Food is served in the bar.

_ _/_ _/20_ _

The Vineyard

Main Street, Blanchardstown, Dublin 15
(1) 821 3109
A traditional local pub, also home to Tournedos Restaurant. Food is served in the bar every day and there is regular entertainment.

_ _/_ _/20_ _

Burnell Bar and Grill

Hilton Airport Hotel, Northern Cross, Malahide Road, Dublin 17
(1) 866 1800
reservations@dublinairporthilton.com
www.hilton.com
Bar and restaurant of The Hilton Airport Hotel, Dublin. Food is served in the bar every day and there is regular entertainment.

_ _/_ _/20_ _

Campion's

Malahide Road, Balgriffin, Dublin 17
(1) 846 0008
A traditional local pub opposite Balgriffin Cemetery. A light snack menu is served and there is regular entertainment.

_ _/_ _/20_ _

Martin's

Clonshaugh Shopping Centre, Clonshaugh Avenue, Clonshaugh/ Priorswood, Dublin 17
(1) 847 7280
A traditional local pub with regular entertainment, previously named The Priorswood. The pub was established in 1974.

_ _/_ _/20_ _

The Newtown House

Newtown Industrial Estate, Malahide Road, Darndale, Dublin 17
(1) 847 2594
A traditional local pub previously called The Belcamp and known locally as The Beller. Food is served on Sundays and there is regular entertainment.

_ _/_ _/20_ _

Southside suburbs

Dublin 4: Ballsbridge, Donnybrook,Belfield, Irishtown, Ringsend and Sandymount

The RDS (Royal Dublin Society) in Ballsbridge is a venue which is used for exhibitions, concerts and sporting events. The Aviva Stadium, Ballsbridge is a sports stadium located on Lansdowne Road. It was built on the site of the old Lansdowne Road Stadium, and can now hold nearly 52,000 spectators. Part of Dublin 4, reaching from Ballsbridge to Merrion Road, Ailesbury Road and Shrewsbury Road, is locally known as the Embassy Belt because of the proliferation of embassies in this area.

Donnybrook is an affluent suburb. RTÉ, the public service broadcaster of Ireland, is based in Donnybrook, and broadcasts both radio and TV to the nation. St Vincent's University Hospital is situated in Elm Park. Next to the public hospital is the newly built ultra-modern St Vincent's Private Hospital.

University College Dublin (UCD) is the country's largest university. Originally located in the city centre, most of its faculties have been relocated to the campus at Belfield.

Irishtown has a nature park that offers a variety of walking trails along the Poolbeg peninsula.

Ringsend is an inner suburb of Dublin. Ringsend and the southern part of Dublin Port are also part of the Great South Wall, which connects Poolbeg Lighthouse to the mainland. This area also contains Dublin's main power station, which has two huge red and white chimneys, a famous Dublin landmark. There has been much development in recent years, including The Grand Canal Dock project. Shelbourne Park is a greyhound racing stadium also based in Ringsend.

Sandymount is a suburb situated along the coastline about 3km from Dublin city. It has many large Victorian houses along with new developments.

Dublin 6: Milltown, Ranelagh, Rathmines, Dartry and Rathgar.

Milltown has an impressive nineteenth-century railway bridge that crosses over the Dodder River. The bridge now serves the Luas tram system. It is also home to the Milltown Institute.

Ranelagh is mainly a residential area. The district was originally a village, surrounded by landed estates. Ranelagh is also home to one of Dublin's Georgian squares. Ranelagh's notable residents have included former Taoiseach Garret FitzGerald, former President Mary Robinson, Nell McCafferty, campaigner and journalist, and Eamon Morrissey, actor.

One of Rathmines' most prominent features is the Town Hall and clock tower, now occupied by Rathmines College. Rathmines is traditionally known as 'flatland', as it provides rented accommodation to many people who work and study in the city. Dartry is a residential area. Trinity Hall is a well-known hall of residence for students of Trinity College Dublin. Also in Dartry is Dartry House, a mansion built in 1840 and owned over time by Obadiah Williams, a wealthy merchant, and Independent Newspapers' William Martin Murphy.

Rathgar is a suburb whose houses are mostly red-brick Victorian and Georgian terraces. Many notable figures lived there, including Countess Markiewicz, James Joyce—who was born in Brighton Square—and former Taoiseach Jack Lynch.

Dublin 6W: Harold's Cross, Kimmage, Templeogue and Terenure

Harold's Cross is an urban village with a large number of shops and residences. It is home to Mount Jerome Cemetery and Our Lady's Hospice which was founded in 1879. The Harold's Cross Greyhound Stadium has been a popular venue for many years, and up to the early 1990s many local football matches were also played here.

Kimmage is a small suburb near Harold's Cross and Rathfarnham. Kimmage spreads across both the Dublin 6W and Dublin 12 postal districts. The most famous landmark is the KCR or Kimmage Crossroads. The river Poddle flows through Kimmage, later flowing into the River Liffey.

Templeogue is situated 6 km from the city centre and the same distance from the Dublin mountains. It contains many housing estates, and several sports clubs.

Terenure is a mainly residential suburb located north of Rathfarnham and south of Harold's Cross. Some of its famous residents include musicians from the band Republic of Loose, Rob Smith and The Coronas, Donal McCann, and James Joyce.

Dublin 8: Phoenix Park, Kilmainham, Portobello, South Circular Road, Dolphin's Barn, The Coombe, Rialto, The Liberties, Inchicore, and Islandbridge

Phoenix Park is the largest public park in Dublin, covering 1,750 acres. There are many features within the park, including:

- Áras an Uachtaráin, the residence of the President of Ireland.
- Dublin Zoo, one of Dublin's most popular tourist attractions. Opened in 1831, it has undergone major renovations and extensions in recent years. The Zoo's grounds cover 59 acres, including a lake area that has been given to the zoo by Áras an Uachtaráin.
- The headquarters of An Garda Siochána, the Irish police force.
- Farmleigh, the State Guest House.
- Several sports grounds.
- Many monuments, including the Papal Cross and the Wellington Monument.
- People's Gardens, an area which contains lakes, childen's playgrounds and Victorian horticulture.
- Extensive areas of grassland and woodlands, and a herd of fallow deer.

Kilmainham is home to Kilmainham Gaol, a former prison and now a museum. Many of the leaders of Irish rebellions were imprisoned here and some were executed in the prison. Famous prisoners include Robert Emmet, Charles Stewart Parnell, Padraig Pearse, and Countess Markiewicz. Also in the area is the Irish Museum of Modern Art (IMMA), Ireland's leading national institution for modern and contemporary art. It was previously the Royal Hospital Kilmainham, a home for retired soldiers.

The Liberties were jurisdictions that existed since the arrival of the Anglo-Normans in the twelfth century. In the seventeenth century weavers moved into the area, with much industry developing as a result. Due to the policies of the day, these industries failed and the residents suffered extreme poverty. Today there has been much redevelopment and rehousing.

The Coombe is a street in the south inner city. In the past, like the Liberties, it had a large woollen and silk weaving industry. Today it is best known for its maternity hospital, the Coombe Women's Hospital, which has now moved to Cork Street.

Christ Church Cathedral is the older of the capital's two medieval cathedrals. Home to the Church of Ireland's Archbishop of Dublin, it is the Cathedral of the Dublin diocese, St Patrick's Cathedral being the National Cathedral of Ireland. It was built in the eleventh century on high ground overlooking the Viking settlement of Wood Quay. St Patrick's Cathedral is the largest church in Ireland, with a 43-metre spire.

Guinness Brewery is the home of Guinness. Founded in 1759, it is located at St James's Gate, James's Street. Also located within the building complex is the Guinness Storehouse. It is a museum dedicated to Guinness, and is Dublin's most popular tourist attraction.

Portobello developed greatly as a suburb in the nineteenth century. Many well-to-do families became established here. Later, many Jews who were refugees from pogroms in Eastern Europe also came to live in the area. Portobello (especially Clanbrassil Street) is often referred to as 'Little Jerusalem' because of this. The area has had many notable residents, including George Bernard Shaw, the painter Jack Butler Yeats, TV presenter Eamonn Andrews, the Irish patriot Lord Edward Fitzgerald, and the actor Barry Fitzgerald.

The South Circular Road runs from Kilmainham to Portobello. Until the eighteenth century most of the area was countryside. When estates such as Emorville and Portobello Gardens were put up for sale, rapid residential development took place from then on. The National Stadium, one of Ireland's best-known boxing venues, is also situated on South Circular Road.

Dolphin's Barn is an inner city suburb. Part of the area extends into the Dublin 12 postal district. Its name comes from a family named Dolphyn who once owned a storehouse there. It is home to one of the city's busiest fire stations.

Rialto is a residential suburb. It is located along the abandoned extension from the Grand Canal to James Street Basin. This was rebuilt to serve the Guinness Brewery. Rialto has its own 'Rialto Bridge' which spans the canal extension.

Inchicore is situated around 5km west of the city centre. Parts of the area extend into Dublin 10 and

Dublin 12 postal districts. Inchicore developed from a small village into an industrial and residential area in the nineteenth century. Inchicore is associated with the national transportation system, one of the major engineering works of the Irish railway network being located here.

Islandbridge and its surrounding area are given this name because of the island that was formed here at the junction of the Camac and Liffey rivers. There was a bridge built at this point back in the fourteenth century, but in the eighteenth century it was swept away in a flood. Its replacement bridge still stands today.

Dublin 10: Ballyfermot

Many major Irish motor distributors are based here. The town is also home to The Ballyfermot School of Further Education. It is often referred to as the Rock School, as it is a third level radio, film and television arts college that offers courses in contemporary music performance and music management. It is also home to the Irish School of Animation. Most recently, Ballyfermot has been in the news due to of one of its residents, Mary Byrne, who was an X-Factor finalist.

Dublin 12: Bluebell, Crumlin, Drimnagh, Perrystown and Walkinstown

Bluebell is a small suburb that has become heavily industrialised, Bluebell Industrial Estate being one of the results of this development. Crumlin has the largest children's hospital in Ireland, Our Lady's Hospital for Sick Children. Notable people associated with the area include writer Brendan Behan, author Christy Brown, and Phil Lynott, singer and leader of the rock band Thin Lizzy.

Drimnagh's modern housing development began in the 1930s, with some houses privately built and a great number built by Dublin Corporation. Drimnagh is home to Drimnagh Castle, which was built in the twelfth century and is famous for being the only castle in Ireland that still has a moat around it.

Perrystown is a small suburb between Terenure and Templeogue. Notable residents include showband singer Sonny Knowles and Niall Quinn, former Irish soccer international.

Walkinstown consists primarily of Dublin City Council-owned residential housing. The Long Mile Road is well known for its car dealerships and commercial outlet stores.

Dublin 14: Churchtown, Clonskeagh, Dundrum, Goatstown, Rathfarnham and Windy Arbour

Churchtown is a residential suburb. It is home to the Nutgrove Shopping Centre. It was the birthplace of actress Maureen O'Hara, playwright J. M. Synge and Seán Lemass, Ireland's third Taoiseach.

Clonskeagh is mainly a residential area. It has several green spaces, and spots on the banks of the Dodder river where people like to fish.

Dundrum is a suburban village and district. The huge complex of Dundrum Town Centre, a large purpose-built shopping centre, opened in 2005. Also in Dundrum is the imposing William Dargan bridge, built to facilitate the Luas tram system.

Goatstown is primarily a residential area, with many housing developments in recent years. The area is centred on a pub called the Goat Grill, which is at the intersection of two roads. There has been a pub on this site since the early eighteenth century. The name 'Goatstown' derived from the goats that were bred there. Their milk was considered excellent for those suffering from tuberculosis.

The suburb of Rathfarnham is home to several historic buildings and parks, including Rathfarnham Castle, Marlay Park, Dodder Park and Bushy Park.

Windy Arbour is a small suburban village surrounded by several housing estates. The most famous person to live there was Robert Emmet, Irish nationalist.

Dublin 16: Ballinteer, Knocklyon, Balally and Rockbrook

Ballinteer has undergone extensive development over recent years. The name Ballinteer means 'Home of the Stonemason'. Part of Ballinteer is bordered by the 300-acre Marley Park.

Knocklyon is a residential suburb. The M50 motorway divides the area, with most of the suburb on the east side. Its focal point is the area comprising supermarket, church and community centre.

Balally is a residential area that was originally farmland. It now consists of several housing estates. The district sits at the foot of the Wicklow mountains.

Rockbrook is a small area, situated south of Ballyboden. The Merry Ploughboy pub has become a popular tourist destination for Irish music and dance. The pub is owned by the Merry Ploughboy traditional music group.

Dublin 18: Cabinteely, Cornelscourt, Carrickmines, Foxrock, Kilternan, Sandyford and Stepaside

Cabinteely is a village surrounded by residential housing.

Cornelscourt is a small suburban area, situated between Cabinteely and Foxrock. It is best known for being the site of Ireland's first superstore, Dunnes Stores Shopping Centre.

Much of the suburb of Carrickmines has been greatly developed in recent years. One of its major features is The Park, a state-of-the-art retail and business park.

Foxrock is an upmarket residential area known for its affluence. Samuel Beckett lived here. It is unusual in Ireland in that the village does not have a pub.

Kilternan is a village at the foot of the Dublin mountains. It is the location of Ireland's only artificial ski slope.

Sandyford is a residential suburb, with a major part of it comprising of the Sandyford Industrial Estate, one of the largest industrial estates in Dublin.

The suburb of Stepaside is at the foot of the Three Rock Mountain. In recent years it has undergone great residential development. A large civic centre and park is due to be built, and the park will be named after Samuel Beckett.

Dublin 20: Chapelizod and Palmerstown

Chapelizod is a village situated within the city of Dublin. Interesting features include St Laurence's Church with its medieval bell tower, and a fine Georgian house where writer Joseph Sheridan Le Fanu worked. It is also the setting of one of James Joyce's short stories.

Palmerstown is located west of the city centre. Over the years much of Palmerstown has been developed for residential, transportation and commercial purposes.

Dublin 22: Clondalkin and Liffey Valley

Clondalkin is located 10 km west of the city centre. It is a busy town with a large population. Clondalkin is also home to an eighth-century round tower, acknowledged as one of the oldest and best preserved in the country.

The extensive Liffey Valley Shopping Centre was developed in 1998. Covering a large area, it contains many large retail outlets and a cinema.

Dublin 24: Firhouse, Jobstown and Tallaght.

Firhouse has developed from a small rural village into an outer suburb of Dublin. It is located close to the foothills of the Dublin mountains.

Jobstown was once a small rural community and over the years has developed into a suburb of Dublin. It is considered as a part of West Tallaght. Jobstown's most famous son is William Russell, who was a well-known war correspondent in the time of Daniel O'Connell.

Tallaght is the largest town in south Dublin, comprising many housing estates. It is home to The Square, one of Ireland's largest shopping centres, with many large retail outlets housed within its complex. It also boasts the Civic Theatre, and Rua Red, a new arts centre for south county Dublin. South of the town is a 6,000-seat soccer ground, Tallaght Stadium.

GUINNESS
KAVANAGH'S
"The Grave Diggers"

The 51

51 Haddington Road, Ballsbridge, Dublin 4
(1) 660 0150
info@the51bar.com
www.the51bar.com
Established in 1843, previously called Paddy Flaherty's, this traditional local pub is a great place to watch sports, especially rugby. It has a large collection of whiskeys of the world. Food is served every day.

_ _/_ _/20_ _

The Bath

26 Bath Avenue, Sandymount, Dublin 4
(1) 667 4687
thebathpub@gmail.com
A traditional vibrant local pub near the Aviva Stadium and previously called Murray's. Food is served every day and there is regular entertainment.

_ _/_ _/20_ _

The Beach Tavern (O'Keeffe's)

9 Bath Street, Irishtown, Dublin 4, (1) 668 0278
raokeeffe@gmail.com
A traditional local pub, a good place to watch sport, and with occasional entertainment. The pictures throughout the pub include rare original Guinness advertisements. Scenes from a number of films have been shot here over the years, the most recent being *Albert Nobbs*. The pub was established in the early 1900s and was previously called Gill's, Kehoe's and Patrick Gleeson and Sons.

_ _/_ _/20_ _

The Beggars Bush

115–119 Haddington Road, Ballsbridge, Dublin 4
(1) 668 2650
A traditional local pub established in 1803 which takes its name from the former barracks on nearby Haddington Road. Food is served every day.

_ _/_ _/20_ _

Bellamy's

13 Ballsbridge Terrace, Ballsbridge, Dublin 4
(1) 668 0397
A traditional local pub near the RDS established in 1853 and housed in a building which bears the date 1859. It was previously called The Embassy Bar and J. Haren's. Food is served every day.

_ _/_ _/20_ _

Bellini's Bar

The Burlington Hotel, Upper Leeson Street, Dublin 4
(1) 618 5600
info@burlingtonhotel.ie, www.burlingtonhotel.ie
This is a very large bar, where food is served every day and there is regular entertainment. The hotel also houses The Mespil Bar, which is used mainly as a residents' bar, The Sussex Restaurant and Le Cirque nightclub, formerly Annabel's and Pure.

_ _/_ _/20_ _

P. J. Branagan's Bar

The Tara Towers Hotel, 4 Merrion Road, Dublin 4
(1) 269 4666
info@taratowers.com
www.taratowers.com
Hotel bar of The Tara Towers Hotel. The lounge has a mix of regulars and hotel patrons. Food is served every day and there is regular entertainment. The hotel also houses The Ocras Restaurant. A good deal of this book was put together here, and both myself and Nicola Sedgwick, my researcher/editor, found the staff very kind and helpful at all times.

_ _/_ _/20_ _

The Chophouse Gastro Pub

2 Shelbourne Road/Bath Ave, Ballsbridge, Dublin 4
(1) 660 2390
info@thechophouse.ie
www.thechophouse.ie
A gastro-pub established in 2009, previously called Hanion's, Rumm's D4 and The Shelbourne Bar.

_ _/_ _/20_ _

John Clarke & Sons

80–82 Irishtown Road, Irishtown, Dublin 4
(1) 660 9072
info@jclarksons.ie
A traditional local pub, serving food every day. It was established in 1932. The pub is also home to The Fusion Bistro.

_ _/_ _/20_ _

Clyde Bar and The Dubliner Bar

Clyde Court Hotel and The Ballsbridge Hotel, Lansdowne Road, Ballsbridge, Dublin 4
(1)238 2700, (1) 637 9300
The Clyde Court Hotel was formerly the Berkeley Court Hotel. The Dubliner Bar is housed in The Ballsbridge Hotel, formerly Ballsbridge Inn and Ballsbridge Towers Hotel. The hotels are built on the grounds of the former Clyde Park. Food is served in the bars every day.

_ _/_ _/20_ _

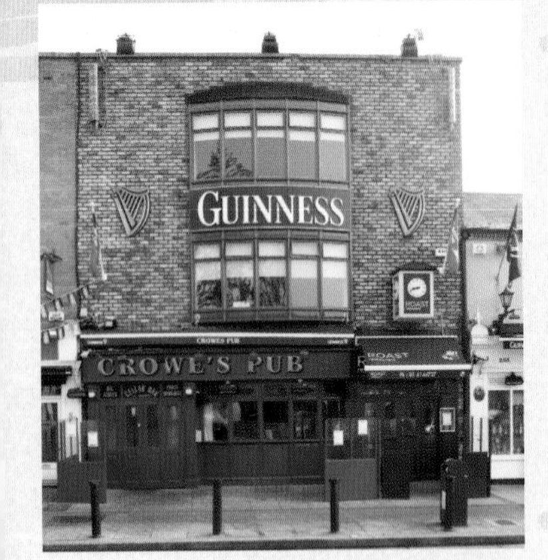

Crowe's Pub

10 Merrion Road, Ballsbridge, Dublin 4
(1) 668 0955
A traditional local pub established in 1908 in the heart of Ballsbridge, near the RDS. There is a restaurant upstairs called Roast. Crowe's is very much a sporting pub, with many sporting pictures, sports clothing and memorabilia throughout the bar.

_ _/_ _/20_ _

Paddy Cullen's and Mary Mac's

12–14 Merrion Road, Ballsbridge, Dublin 4
(1) 668 4492
info@paddycullens.com
www.paddycullens.com
Previously called The Exhibition House here are two pubs in one--Paddy Cullen's and Mary Mac's. They are both traditional local sports pubs, once owned by Paddy Cullen, the famous Dublin Gaelic footballer of the 1970s. Food is served every day and there is regular entertainment.

_ _/_ _/20_ _

The Den Bar

The Lansdowne Hotel, 27–29 Pembroke Road, Ballsbridge, Dublin 4, (1) 668 2522
reception@lansdownehotel.ie, www.lansdownehotel.ie
A traditional hotel bar with lots of sport memorabilia on display. Food is served every day and there is regular entertainment. The bar was once called The Pirates' Den Bar and Grill. The hotel also houses The Druid's Restaurant.

_ _/_ _/20_ _

Doyle's of Irishtown

68a Irishtown Road, Irishtown, Dublin 4
A traditional local pub, established in 1940 and previously called The Irishtown House, O'Dwyer's and The Seapoint House. It had been closed for about three years before reopening as Doyle's in 2010. A light snack menu is served and there is regular entertainment.

_ _/_ _/20_ _

The Dylan Cocktail Bar and Terraces

The Dylan Hotel, Eastmoreland Place, Ballsbridge, Dublin 4, (1) 660 3000
justask@dylan.ie, www.dylan.ie
This boutique hotel is housed in a building that was previously the nurses' home of the Royal City of Dublin Hospital (Baggot Street Hospital). Food is served in the bar every day.

_ _/_ _/20_ _

The Gasworks

The Grand Canal Hotel, Grand Canal Street, Ballsbridge, Dublin 4
(1) 646 1000
reservations@grandcanalhotel.ie
www.grandcanalhotel.ie
This bar in the Grand Canal Hotel was previously called Kitty O'Shea's and Smyth's of Grand Canal Street. A pub has traded here since circa 1860. Food is served every day and there is regular entertainment. The hotel is also home to Epic Restaurant.

_ _/_ _/20_ _

Hampton Bar

Hampton Hotel, 19–29 Morehampton Road, Donnybrook, Dublin 4
(1) 668 0995
info@hamptonhotel.ie www.vanillanightclub.com
www.hamptonhotel.ie
This hotel, previously Sachs Hotel, with its Georgian Bar and Sachs Nightclub, reopened under the Hamptons name in 2009 as a boutique hotel with a stylish candlelit cocktail bar / bistro. It is also home to Vanilla Boutique nightclub which opened in 2010.

_ _/_ _/20_ _

Herbert Park Hotel Bar and Terrace Lounge

Herbert Park Hotel, Ballsbridge Terrace, Ballsbridge, Dublin 4
(1) 667 2200
reservations@herbertparkhotel.ie
www.herbertparkhotel.ie
Situated close to the RDS in Ballsbridge the hotel is also home to The Pavilion Restaurant.

_ _/_ _/20_ _

Hobbler's End and Raytown Bar

12 Bridge Street, Ringsend, Dublin 4
Named after 'hobblers', men who rowed out to sea on foggy nights to guide in ships for a fee, this traditional local pub is currently closed. Its previous name was Bunit and Simpson, after names found carved or written in the cellar during renovations. Prior to that the pub was called North's and also O'Dwyer's.

_ _/_ _/20_ _

Horse Show House (Madigan's)

34–36 Merrion Road, Ballsbridge, Dublin 4
(1) 668 9424
www.madigan.ie
Madigan's Horse Show House is a traditional local pub and sports bar situated opposite the RDS. The pub is 'the home of Leinster Rugby'. Food is served every day.

_ _/_ _/20_ _

The Ice Bar and The Lobby Lounge

The Four Seasons Hotel, Simmonscourt Road, Ballsbridge, Dublin 4, (1) 665 4000
reservations.dublin@fourseasons.com
www.fourseasons.com/dublin
The modern stylish Ice Bar is open Wednesdays to Sundays, and serves tapas, wines and cocktails. The Lobby Lounge serves light refreshments, cocktails, and afternoon teas, with piano playing on weekdays. It also stocks a large selection of whiskeys. The hotel also houses the Seasons Restaurant.

_ _/_ _/20_ _

Kiely's of Donnybrook

22–24 Donnybrook Road, Donnybrook, Dublin 4
(1) 283 0209
www.kielysofdonnybrook.ie
A traditional local bar and lounge which has traded as Kiely's since 1945. It was established in the early 1700s and granted a licence in 1739. A section of the pub is called Ciss Madden's Bar. Food is served every day and there is regular entertainment.

_ _/_ _/20_ _

The Lansdowne

14 Bath Avenue, Ballsbridge, Dublin 4
(1) 668 0906
A traditional local pub near The Aviva Stadium. It has regular entertainment including Monday afternoon traditional music sessions. Food is served every day. The pub was established in 1845.

_ _/_ _/20_ _

The Leeson Lounge

148 Upper Leeson Street, Dublin 4
(1) 660 3816
A traditional local sports pub with many pictures of GAA and sporting events throughout the house. A light snack menu is served and there is regular entertainment.

_ _/_ _/20_ _

Long's

48–48A Donnybrook Road, Donnybrook, Dublin 4
(1) 269 2426
A traditional local pub that dates dack to 1861. A light snack menu is served and there is occasional entertainment.

__/__/20__

Lonnegan's Bar

The Montrose Hotel, Stillorgan Road,
Stillorgan, Dublin 4
This hotel bar has been closed since 2010.

__/__/20__

McCloskey's

83–85 Morehampton Road, Donnybrook, Dublin 4
(1) 668 4345
Known locally as Mac's this traditional local pub is housed in a building that dates back to 1901. Food is served seven days a week—Mac's is famous for its Irish stew.

__/__/20__

The Merrion Inn

188 Merrion Road, Ballsbridge, Dublin 4
(1) 269 3816
info@themerrioninn.com
www.themerrioninn.com
The Merrion Inn is a traditional local pub, serving food every day and with a large selection of craft beers. It is situated opposite St Vincent's Hospital. The pub, which is currently closed due to fire, is run by the McCormack family who have been in the pub trade since 1941. It was previously called TV Brady and Co.

__/__/20__

Mulligan's of Sandymount

86 Sandymount Road, Sandymount, Dublin 4
(1) 660 2061
A newly-built traditional local pub opened in 2007. Food is served every day and it is a good place to watch sports. Previously there was a pub called Jack Maclean's on or near this site.

_ _/_ _/20_ _

The Oarsman Bar & Brasserie

8 Bridge Street, Ringsend, Dublin 4
(1) 668 9360
The well-finished interior of this traditional local pub is embellished with old clocks throughout. The pub was established in 1820. Food is served every day and there is regular entertainment.

_ _/_ _/20_ _

M. O'Brien's

8–9 Sussex Terrace, Upper Leeson Street, Dublin 4
(1) 676 2851
info@m-obriens.ie
www.m-obriens.ie
A traditional local pub, established circa 1900. It is also home to The Sussex Restaurant which is located on the first floor. This pub was renovated to a high standard in 2008. Food is served every day and there is regular entertainment.

_ _/_ _/20_ _

Ocean Bar and Restaurant

Millennium Tower, Charlotte Quay Dock, Ringsend, Dublin 4
(1) 668 8862
info@oceanbar.ie
www.oceanbar.ie
A modern lounge bar in a unique waterside setting in front of the Grand Canal Dock, near the Bord Gáis Energy Theatre. Food is served every day. It is not unusual to find people paying chess here.

_ _/_ _/20_ _

O'Connell's

135 Morehampton Road, Donnybrook, Dublin 4
(1) 269 6116
info@oconnellsdonnybrook.com
www.oconnellsdonnybrook.com

This pub was established in 1922 and was previously called Madigan's. The O'Connells, who had been trading in Ballsbridge since 1999, opened the traditional local bar and restaurant here in November 2010.

_ _/_ _/20_ _

O'Reilly's

Seafort Avenue, Sandymount, Dublin 4
(1) 668 3675

A traditional local pub, established in 1922. A light snack menu is served on weekdays and there is regular entertainment.

_ _/_ _/20_ _

Sandymount House (Ryan's)

1 Sandymount Green, Sandymount, Dublin 4
(1) 269 5026

This traditional local pub was established in 1899 as Ryan's—coincidentally the same name as that of the current owners, who have traded here since circa 1977. The pub was previously called Fagan's and Healon's. Some scenes from the film *The Tiger's Tail* were shot here. Food is served every day.

_ _/_ _/20_ _

The Schoolhouse

The Schoolhouse Hotel, 2–8 Northumberland Road,
Ballsbridge, Dublin 4, (1) 667 5014
info@schoolhousehotel.com
www.schoolhousehotel.com

Built as a schoolhouse in 1892, this building beside Mount Street Bridge was converted into a gastro pub, hotel and restaurant in 1998. The bar has a high ceiling with timber beams and there is a mezzanine on one side of the room. There is regular entertainment.

_ _/_ _/20_ _

William Searson's

42–44 Upper Baggot Street, Dublin 4, (1) 660 0330
info@chawkegroup.ie

Also known as Searson's of Baggot Street this is a traditional local sports bar that attracts a big rugby crowd. 'Every pass . . . Every kick . . . Every ruck . . . Every maul . . . Every point . . . Every try . . . See it at Searson's.' Food is served every day. This pub was established in 1845.

_ _/_ _/20_ _

The Shipwright

16–20 Thorncastle Street, Ringsend, Dublin 4
(1) 668 1100
contact@shipwright-ringsend.com
www.shipwright-ringsend.com

Also known as Sally's Return, this is a traditional local pub with rooms. It was previously called Fagan's. There is regular entertainment.

_ _/_ _/20_ _

Slattery's Public House

62 Upper Grand Canal St, Sandymount, Dublin 4
(1) 668 5481

Known locally as Slatt's this is a traditional local pub where five roads merge and rugby begins in the neighbourhood of the Aviva Stadium, Lansdowne Road. 'The Real Rugby Pub.' Lunch is served on weekdays.

_ _/_ _/20_ _

Smyth's of Haddington Road

10 Haddington Road, Ballsbridge, Dublin 4
(1) 660 6305
info@courtneyslounge.com
www.courtneyslounge.com
A traditional local pub. Many famous Irish writers drank here in the past. It was established around 1912. Food is served every day.

_ _/_ _/20_ _

The Terrace Bar

The Mespil Hotel, Mespil Road, Ballsbridge, Dublin 4
(1) 488 4600
mespil@leehotels.com, www.leehotels.com
The bar of The Mespil Hotel which is also home to The Glaze Bistro. The hotel is located opposite the Grand Canal near Baggot Street Bridge.

_ _/_ _/20_ _

Tom's Bar

Bewley's Hotel, Merrion Road, Ballsbridge, Dublin 4, (1) 668 1111
ballsbridge@bewleyshotels.com, www.bewleyshotels.com
The hotel is situated near the RDS. It houses a restaurant as well as the bar, and the Thomas Prior Hall Banqueting and Conference Centre. Bewley's started out as a tea and coffee emporium in 1840, expanding into hotels in recent years.

_ _/_ _/20_ _

Tritonville Bar and Terracer

Sandymount Hotel, Herbert Road, Sandymount, Dublin 4
(1) 668 4321
info@sandymounthotel.ie, www.sandymounthotel.ie
This hotel was established in 1955 in eight Victorian houses and was called The Mount Herbert until 2011. It is five minutes' walk to the Aviva Stadium. The hotel also houses The Cordyline Restaurant, which is generally used by residents and is available for functions. Food is served in the bar every day.

_ _/_ _/20_ _

The Vintage Inn

74 Irishtown Road, Irishtown, Dublin 4
(1) 668 9621
A traditional local pub with a great gallery of paintings all around the bar. A picture of Brendan Behan in the bar has a quote which reads, 'I only drink twice: once when I'm thirsty and once when I'm not'. The pub was previously called Murtagh's and O'Donoghue's. A picture of the pub in the bar dates it back to 1891. Lunch is served every day.

_ _/_ _/20_ _

The Waterloo Bar & Grill

36 Upper Baggot Street, Dublin 4
(1) 660 0650
info@thewaterloobarandgrill.ie
www.thewaterloobarandgrill.ie
A traditional local gastro pub established in 1845. It is a long bar with murals of neighbouring shops and Baggot Street Hospital. There is regular entertainment.

_ _/_ _/20_ _

The Wellington

1a Upper Baggot Street, Dublin 4
(1) 660 7344
Many famous writers used to drink in this traditional local pub. It was previously called Cheers, The Crocket Bobby, GF Handels and Dessie Hynes. A light snack menu is served on weekdays and there is regular entertainment.

_ _/_ _/20_ _

The Yacht

8 Thorncastle Street, Ringsend, Dublin 4
(1) 668 0977
A traditional local pub where patrons will sing at any time at the drop of a hat. This pub was established in 1889.

_ _/_ _/20_ _

Ashton's

11 Vergemount, Clonskeagh, Dublin 6
(1) 283 0045
This traditional local bar and bistro is a popular lunch spot and a good place to watch sports, especially rugby.

_ _/_ _/20_ _

Birchall's of Ranelagh

129 Ranelagh, Dublin 6
(1) 497 3985
info@mangangroupe.ie

Birchall's was an old haunt of Flann O'Brien's and is still popular with the many academic, media and literary people living in Ranelagh. It was established in 1850 and was previously called Ranelagh House and Jack Birchall's. It's a comfortable local traditional pub serving food every day and with occasional entertainment.

_ _/_ _/20_ _

Rody Boland's

12–14 Upper Rathmines Road, Rathmines, Dublin 6
(01) 497 0328
www.rodybolands.com
Renowned for food and craic this is a large traditional local pub filled with old pictures, musical instruments and sporting memorabilia. Established in 1873, it was previously called The Concorde, Thomas Kennedy's, and Street's. Food is served every day and there is regular entertainment.

_ _/_ _/20_ _

Coman's

2–6 Terenure Road East, Rathgar, Dublin 6
(1) 490 3501
comanshouse@live.ie
Part of this traditional local pub, The Bottler's Bar, used to house a branch of the Munster and Leinster Bank. The pub was established in 1847. It serves food every day and has entertainment occasionally.

_ _/_ _/20_ _

Copán

304 Lower Rathmines Road, Rathmines, Dublin 6, (1) 406 0218
info@copan.ie, www.copan.ie
Copán Café Bar and Garden Terrace is a large modern bar opened in 2010. It takes its name from the ancient Mayan city of Copan in Western Honduras, and the decor reflects this theme. The building itself dates back to 1845, a date written in the brickwork above the door which also bears the name 'Leinster House'. It was previously called Madigan's and The Madison Bar. Food is served every day, and there is regular entertainment.

_ _/_ _/20_ _

Corrigan's Mount Pleasant Inn

27–28 Lower Mount Pleasant Ave, Rathmines, Dublin 6
themountpleasantinn@gmail.com
Just off the main stretch of Rathmines, this traditional local pub was established in 1910. It was previously called Guinan's, and still bears this name in the brickwork. The pub offers regular entertainment.

_ _/_ _/20_ _

The Dropping Well

Classon's Bridge, Milltown Road,
Dublin 6, (1) 497 3969
info@droppingwell.com
This well-known historic pub was established in 1847 on the site of a former morgue on the banks of the Dodder River. You can see the statue 'Woody The Adopted Rhino' in the centre of the river. It is used to see how high the water is rising, since the area is vulnerable to flooding. A section of the pub, Boxer Maher's Bar, is for sportslovers. Food is served every day in The Well Lounge and there is entertainment on Saturdays. There is another statue at the front of the pub, Rosie at the Well.

_ _/_ _/20_ _

Grace's

2–5 Rathgar Road, Rathmines, Dublin 6
(1) 497 4199
A traditional local pub, previously called O'Byrne's. The upstairs bar is called The Loft. Food is served on weekdays and there is regular entertainment.

_ _/_ _/20_ _

The Hill

1 Old Mount Pleasant, Ranelagh, Dublin 6, (1) 497 6333
This traditional local pub, which was established in 1845, was previously called Kennedy's and McGrath's. The author of *Goodbye to the Hill,* Lee Dunne, was a native of the area locally known as 'the Hill'. He told me: 'I rode down that hill six mornings a week for three years vowing in my pauper's heart "some day I'm going to say goodbye to this effing place", and so books are born.' Lee Dunne did 'the Knowledge' and drove a black cab in London for a number of years.

_ _/_ _/20_ _

Humphrey's

79–81 Ranelagh, Dublin 6
(1) 497 2490
humphreysranelaghltd@eircom.net
Established circa 1910 as Tim Humphrey's Bar and Grocer this is a traditonal local pub.

_ _/_ _/20_ _

McSorley's

1–5 Sandford Road, Ranelagh, Dublin 6
(1) 497 9775
d6bar@yahoo.ie
Previously called McCauley's and The Sandford House this modern bar and lounge is a good place to watch sports. It is home to The Ken Doherty Tribute Room where you will find a gallery of photographs of local man Ken Doherty's snooker career, including his World Championship win in 1997. The Wild Goose Restaurant is next door.

_ _/_ _/20_ _

Mother Reilly's Bar

26–30 Upper Rathmines Road, Rathmines, Dublin 6, (1) 497 5486
enquiries@uppercrosshousehotel.com
www.uppercrosshousehotel.com
Housed within The Upper Cross Hotel this is a traditional local bar, filled with artefacts which makes it look as though it has been there for centuries. The hotel was previously a bed & breakfast; in the mid-1990s it was changed into a hotel, and the bar was added. The bar has since been well extended. The hotel is also home to The Upper Circle Restaurant.

_ _/_ _/20_ _

Murphy's

93–95 Upper Rathmines Road, Rathmines, Dublin 6
(1) 497 4066
Trading as Murphy's since 2000 this traditional local pub was previously called Dawson's, McCarthy's and Ward's. The pub was established circa 1760. Food is served every day and there is regular entertainment.

_ _/_ _/20_ _

The Orwell Hotel

69 Orwell Road, Rathgar, Dublin 6
(1) 492 2444
The bar of the Orwell Hotel, which also houses Bistro No 69. The hotel was previously called The Carrick Hall Hotel and was then home to TK's Bar and Restaurant. The building dates back to around 1885.

_ _/_ _/20_ _

O'Shea's of Clonskeagh

68 Clonskeagh Road, Clonskeagh, Dublin 6
(1) 269 8250
jimclonshhse@eircom.net
Established in 1893, this is a traditional local pub. Food is served every day, and there is entertainment on the first Sunday of the month.

_ _/_ _/20_ _

Russell's

60 Ranelagh, Dublin 6
(1) 497 7120
russellsofranelagh@eircom.net
A traditional local pub with a fine first floor terrace for smokers. For a long time, there was a chalkboard in the window that said 'Russell's: The Alcohol-Themed Bar.' Food is served every day and there is regular entertainment.

_ _/_ _/20_ _

Slatterys of Rathmines

217 Lower Rathmines Road, Rathmines, Dublin 6
(1) 497 2052
slatterysrathmines@gmail.com
On my visits to this traditional local pub and music venue I found great staff and customer banter. There is regular entertainment.

_ _/_ _/20_ _

Smyth's of Ranelagh

75–77 Ranelagh, Dublin 6
(1) 491 1075
A traditional local pub previously called Lister's and M. O'Brien's. Smyth's serves food every day and offers regular entertainment.

_ _/_ _/20_ _

Stout Bar

82 Lower Rathmines Road, Rathmines, Dublin 6
This traditional bar and lounge is currently closed. It was previously called Brady's, Quinn's and The Rathmines Inn.

_ _/_ _/20_ _

Toast Café Bar

196 Lower Rathmines Road, Rathmines, Dublin 6
(1) 412 6285
toastcafebar@live.ie
A modern local pub, which used to be a fire station. It was previously called Curtin's, The Lancer, Lavin's and The Station. The proprietor told me the pub may have been called Campion's, which was the pub mentioned in Lee Dunne's book, *Goodbye to the Hill*. Food is served every day and there is regular entertainment.

_ _/_ _/20_ _

The Tram

121 Lower Rathmines Road, Rathmines, Dublin 6
A large bar and club set over three floors. It previously traded as The Days Inn Hotel. This pub is currently closed.

_ _/_ _/20_ _

Brady's

5–9 Terenure Place, Terenure, Dublin 6W
(1) 492 0141
A traditional local pub established in 1962, offering food every day and regular entertainment. A section of the pub called Gub Dandys is a live music venue. The Ken Doherty Snooker Academy, opened in 2011 by the former World Snooker Champion, is located behind the pub.

_ _/_ _/20_ _

D'Arcy McGee's

Spawell Leisure Complex, Wellington Lane, Templeogue, Dublin 6W, (1) 490 7727
info@darcymcgees.ie, www.darcymcgees.ie
Previously called The Spawell Bar this is a traditional pub and venue located in the Spawell sports complex. It has a snooker room. Food is served every day and there is regular entertainment.

_ _/_ _/20_ _

The H Crossbar

238 Harold's Cross Road, Harold's Cross, Dublin 6W
(1) 499 5650
A traditional local pub, previously called Quinn's. For a short time in 2011 it traded as Molly Molloy's, but then changed back to The H Crossbar.

_ _/_ _/20_ _

McGowan's of Harold's Cross

174–176 Harolds Cross Road, Harold's Cross, Dublin 6W
(1) 497 8618
This is a traditional local pub, established in 1780. It was previously called The Inn in the Park and The Park Inn. Food is served every day and there is occasional entertainment.

_ _/_ _/20_ _

The Morgue

176 Templeogue Road, Templeogue Village, Dublin 6W
(1) 490 5813
This pub, which was established in 1848, gets its name from a morbid practice in the time when the old tram line used to run beside it. After fatal accidents, tram workers would bring the corpses into the pub and lay them out on the marble countertop. The traditional local pub contains Reeves Restaurant on the first floor. There is regular entertainment.

_ _/_ _/20_ _

Peggy Kelly's

161 Harold's Cross Road, Harold's Cross, Dublin 6W
(1) 497 2445
A traditional local pub near Harold's Cross Greyhound Stadium. It was established circa 1900 and was previously called Flanagan's, The Greyhound and O'Dwyer's. Food is served every day and there is regular entertainment.

_ _/_ _/20_ _

The Rathgar

Terenure Road East, Rathgar, Dublin 6W
(1) 490 6044
Originally established in 1851 this traditional local bar was previously called The 108 and Martin Murphy & Sons. It reopened in 2010 as The Rathgar after being completely rebuilt. Food is served every day and there is regular entertainment.

_ _/_ _/20_ _

Rosie O'Grady's

282 Harold's Cross Road, Harold's Cross, Dublin 6W
(1) 492 2239
This traditional local pub was established in 1803. Food is served every day and there is regular entertainment.

_ _/_ _/20_ _

Seán Mac D's

69 Harold's Cross Road, Harold's Cross, Dublin 6W
(1) 497 6832
Still known locally by its older name, The Lantern, this is a traditional local pub and venue. It was closed a few years ago, and reopened for a short time as an off-licence in 2009. It opened again as a pub, Paddy's Bar, in 2010. Food is served every day and there is regular entertainment.

_ _/_ _/20_ _

The Terenure Inn

94–96 Terenure Road North, Terenure, Dublin 6W
(1) 490 7552
A traditional local pub and restaurant, previously called Fitzpatrick's. Food is served every day in the bar and there is regular entertainment.

_ _/_ _/20_ _

The Two Sisters

2–6 Wainsfort Drive, Kimmage, Dublin 6W
(1) 490 0166
twosisters@eircom.net
Devitt's The Two Sisters is a family-run traditional local pub, serving food every day. There is occasional entertainment, generally on the last Friday of the month.

_ _/_ _/20_ _

Vaughan's Eagle House

DUBLIN TOURISM
MOTHER OF
JAMES JOYCE
MAY MURRAY
BORN HERE IN MAY 1859

105–107 Terenure Road North, Terenure,
Dublin 6W, (1) 490 1251
vaughanseatery@gmail.com, www.vaughanseatery.ie
James Joyce's mother, May Murray, was born in this house in 1859. The traditional local pub was established in 1916. Its previous name was The Catalonia. Food from Vaughan's Eatery is served every day, and there is regular entertainment.

_ _/_ _/20_ _

4 Corners Bar and Terrace

The Hilton Hotel, Inchicore Road, Kilmainham,
Dublin 8, (1) 420 1800
reservations.dublinkilmainham@hilton.com
www.dublinkilmainham.hilton.com
A contemporary hotel bar and restaurant. The hotel, which opened in 2007, overlooks Kilmainham Gaol Museum and is near IMMA (the Irish Museum of Modern Art). The Cinnamon Restaurant is also housed within the hotel.

_ _/_ _/20_ _

The Ardee House

1 Chamber Street, Dublin 8
Tucked away off Cork Street in a quiet location, this traditional local pub was previously called Murphy's. It is currently closed.

_ _/_ _/20_ _

Arthur's

28 Thomas Street, Dublin 8
(1) 454 2506
A traditional local pub near the Guinness Storehouse, previously called Gleeson's Public House, G. F. Handel, Paddy Ryan's and Ryan Brothers. The pub was closed for about six years and reopened on 17 March 2011. Food is served every day and there is regular entertainment.

_ _/_ _/20_ _

Baker's

48 Thomas Street, Dublin 8
(1) 473 6789
This atmospheric pub in the heart of the Liberties is frequented by many local characters. It was named Nash's for some years but in 2010 reverted to its original name. Food is served every day and there is regular entertainment.

_ _/_ _/20_ _

The Barley Mow

Francis Street, Dublin 8
A traditional local pub. It is currently closed.

_ _/_ _/20_ _

The Bayno

101 Francis Street, Dublin 8
A traditional local pub in the heart of the Liberties, currrently closed. It used to be called The Silken Thomas but was demolished and completely rebuilt. When it reopened as The Bayno, the new owners furnished part of the interior with items from The Scholars pub off Clanbrassil Street, which is now closed. The new name came from the nearby Iveagh Play Centre in Bull Alley Street, which was known as The Beano. From 1913, this centre provided education and social skills to Dubliners.

_ _/_ _/20_ _

The Bird Flanagan (O'Shea's)

471–477 South Circular Road,
Rialto, Dublin 8, (1) 453 2797
lukebyrne@hotmail.com
O'Shea's traditional local pub is named after Willie The 'Bird' Flanagan (born 1867) who was a notorious Dublin character and joker. He is said to have ridden his horse into the bar of the Gresham Hotel and demanded a drink—for the horse. I am told the pub was once called The County Bar. Food is served on weekdays and there is regular entertainment.

_ _/_ _/20_ _

The Black Horse Inn (Kelly's)

233 Tyrconnell Road, Inchicore, Dublin 8
(1) 454 3939
Kelly's the Black Horse Inn is a traditional local pub established in 1845. A sign in the bar reads 'There's no F in parking'. Light snacks are served during the week and there is occasional entertainment.

_ _/_ _/20_ _

The Brazen Head

20 Lower Bridge Street, Dublin 8, (1) 679 5186
info@brazenhead.com, www.brazenhead.com
Believed to be Ireland's oldest pub, dating back to 1198, this traditional bar and restaurant is a unique old inn full of character, with great music sessions every night, and two sessions on Sundays in the bar or the Music Room. There are storytelling sessions on Sunday afternoons. Many famous Irish writers drank here in the past, and today its patrons include many famous names.

_ _/_ _/20_ _

The Brewery Bar

8 Newport Street, Dublin 8
(1) 454 1215
A traditional local pub near the Guinness Storehouse and Brewery. There is regular entertainment.

_ _/_ _/20_ _

Carrigan's

72 Old Kilmainham Road, Kilmainham, Dublin 8
A traditional local pub established in 1837. It was previously called Muldowney and Sons. A light snack menu is served and there is occasional entertainment.

_ _/_ _/20_ _

The Clock

111 Thomas Street, Dublin 8
Old clocks tick and chime throughout the bar of this traditional local pub. There are over 50 of them, all keeping good time. The pub was previously called Harrington's but has traded as The Clock since the mid-1970s. A light snack menu is served and there is regular entertainment.

_ _/_ _/20_ _

Coffey's

97 Emmet Road, Dublin 8
A traditional local pub, also known as The Capital Bar, with regular entertainment. It was previously known as Malone's and Vaughan's.

_ _/_ _/20_ _

The Dean Swift

40 Francis Street, Dublin 8
(1) 453 3519
A traditional local pub in the heart of the Liberties, established in 1769. The pub was called O'Connor's many years ago. There is regular entertainment.

_ _/_ _/20_ _

Dillon's The Black and Amber Inn

South Circular Road, Island Bridge, Dublin 8
A traditional local pub. It is currently closed.

_ _/_ _/20_ _

Dillon's The Black Lion

207 Emmet Road, Inchicore, Dublin 8, (1) 453 4580
dillonspubs.info@gmail.com
www.dillonspubs.info
There is sports memorabilia throughout this traditional local sports pub. Originally called The Black Lyon the pub has also traded under the names Egan's, Hardy's, McCann's and McEvoy's. It was established in 1734 as a coaching inn and is the oldest pub in Inchicore. Food is served and there is regular entertainment.

_ _/_ _/20_ _

Donoghue's

29 Emmet Road, Inchicore, Dublin 8
(1) 453 2038
Donoghue's Glen of Aherloe Bar and Lounge is a traditional local pub. A light snack menu is served and there is regular entertainment.

_ _/_ _/20_ _

Fallon's The Capstan Bar

129 The Coombe, Dublin 8
(1) 454 2801
fallons@indigo.ie
This genuine traditional Liberties bar, established circa 1600 used to be a dockers' bar. 'Capstan' refers to a device used to tighten ropes in a ship's rigging. The bar has old-style gas heaters suspended from the ceiling, which are still very effective. The gas lights are still operational— if you visit during a power outage, the staff will switch them on to keep the pub lit! A light snack menu is served.

_ _/_ _/20_ _

Grainger's The Fountain

61–63 Meath St, Dublin 8
(1) 473 7835
A traditional local pub run by the Grainger family who have been trading in Dublin since 1960. Food is served every day and there is regular entertainment.

_ _/_ _/20_ _

The Galway Hooker

Heuston Station, Dublin 8
(1) 670 3463
A traditional pub in Heuston Station, serving food every day, with a coffee bar on the station concourse.

_ _/_ _/20_ _

The Garda Club

8 Harrington Street, Dublin 8
(1) 820 7888
Despite not looking like a pub from the outside, there is indeed a traditional bar inside. Established in 1964 this social club bar for Garda members is open to the general public. There is occasional entertainment.

_ _/_ _/20_ _

Grays of Newmarket Square

Newmarket/Brabazon Street, Dublin 8
A traditional local pub, currently closed.

_ _/_ _/20_ _

The Harold House

35 Clanbrassil Street, Dublin 8
(1) 453 4529
A traditional local pub established circa 1840. It was called Carroll Brothers some decades ago.

_ _/_ _/20_ _

The Headline Bar

56–57 Lower Clanbrassil Street/Leonard's Corner, Dublin 8
(1) 453 4176
Journalists from *The Irish Times* used to drink in this traditional local pub which has many framed newspaper headline cuttings on the walls throughout. The pub was previously called McNally's and Thomas Keogh's Bar and Grocer. Food is served every day and there is occasional entertainment.

_ _/_ _/20_ _

The Hill Top

131 Thomas Street, Dublin 8
A traditional local pub. It traded as an off-licence for a number of years and reopened as a pub in 2010. It was previously called The Robert Emmet, The Hill Top, The Loft, Meagher's, and The Wig and Pen. A light snack menu is served and there is regular entertainment.

_ _/_ _/20_ _

Horse & Jockey

107 Emmet Road, Inchicore, Dublin 8
A traditional local pub, currently closed.

_ _/_ _/20_ _

The Inntro Bar

Jury's Inn, Christchurch Place, Christchurch, Dublin 8
(1) 454 0000
info@jurys.com
www.jurysinns.com
Situated opposite Christchurch Cathedral the hotel houses Infusion Restaurant and Il Barista Coffee as well as The Inntro Bar.

_ _/_ _/20_ _

The Irish House Party

19 Francis Street, Dublin 8, (1) 672 9272
info@theirishhouseparty.com, www.theirishhouseparty.com
A music pub, opened in 2012, which aims to capture the atmosphere of an authentic Irish house party. It was previously called The Green Lizard and The Iveagh. Many of the traditional musicians who play here are all-Ireland champions. The group previously played in various venues around Dublin. They have been highly recommended by Nobel prize-winning poet Seamus Heaney and pianist John O'Conor. Food is served upstairs in their restaurant.

_ _/_ _/20_ _

The Iveagh Lounge

The Ashling Hotel, Parkgate Street, Dublin 8, (1) 677 2324
info@ashlinghotel.ie, www.ashlinghotel.ie
This hotel bar was previously called The Guinness Lounge. Food is served every day. The hotel is located close to Heuston Station and is also home to the Chesterfield Brasserie.

_ _/_ _/20_ _

Judge Darley's

Parkgate Street, Dublin 8
This pub is now a residential home. Its previous names were Kirwan House and Urlingham's.

_ _/_ _/20_ _

Joe's Bar

The Phoenix Park Hotel, 38–39 Parkgate Street, Dublin 8
(1) 679 9769
info@phoenixparkhotel.ie
01 6729272
This family-run hotel used to be The Phoenix Park Guest House and had no bar. The establishment became a hotel after being extensively renovated in conjunction with the hit TV show 'At Your Service' and Joe's Bar opened in 2011. The hotel is also home to Berry Lane Bistro.

_ _/_ _/20_ _

Kate McCauley's

Malpas Court, Lower Clanbrassil Street, Dublin 8
(1) 453 6375
A traditional local pub with regular entertainment.

_ _/_ _/20_ _

Kavanagh's

35 New South Street, Dublin 8
A traditional local pub previously called Farrell's and Kavanagh's. It was closed for several years and reopened in 2011. There is regular entertainment.

_ _/_ _/20_ _

Tom Kennedy's Lounge

65 Thomas Street, Dublin 8
(1) 454 6366
Previously called O'Neill's this traditional local pub is full of Liberties' characters. There is always good craic here. A light snack menu is served and there is regular entertainment.

_ _/_ _/20_ _

Kenny's Lounge

173–174 James's Street, Dublin 8
(1) 677 0753
A traditional local pub situated near St James's Hospital. This pub was previously called Davy's. Food is served every day and there is regular entertainment.

_ _/_ _/20_ _

The Lamplighter

79 The Coombe, Dublin 8
(1) 454 2246
Brady's The Lamplighter is a traditional local pub in the Liberties. Its name comes from a law passed in Dublin in the early 1600s that every fifth house had to display a candle to guide passing travellers. The pub, which dates back to the early 1800s, was previously called The Weavers, as at one time The Coombe was home to the Liberty weavers. There is regular entertainment.

_ _/_ _/20_ _

The Lark Inn

80–81 Meath Street, Dublin 8
(1) 454 2484
Larkin's The Lark Inn is a traditional local pub previously called Kennedy's. A light snack menu is served and there is occasional entertainment.

_ _/_ _/20_ _

Leonard's Corner Café Bar

117 South Circular Road, Dublin 8
(1) 454 2332
Promising 'Good food and beer served with a friendly service' this is a traditional local pub with regular entertainment.

_ _/_ _/20_ _

The Liberty Bar

78 Meath Street, Dublin 8
This traditional local pub in the heart of the Liberties opened as The Liberty Bar in 2010. It traded as an off-licence for a short time and before that it was a pub called Bohan's and Harrington's.

_ _/_ _/20_ _

The Liberty Belle

33 Francis Street, Dublin 8
libertybelle@dublin.ie
Local families have been drinking in this traditional local Liberties pub for generations, many of them sitting in the same seat every time they visit. It has regular entertainment and is a good place to watch sport.

_ _/_ _/20_ _

The Little Green Bar and Café

High Street, Dublin 8
www.littlegreen.ie
A music pub in the Liberties, previously called Ryan's, The Pale and most recently U Bar. Food is served and there is regular entertainment which includes cultural and historical talks. The Pale referred to the area around Dublin that in medieval times was bounded by a fortified ditch and rampart.

_ _/_ _/20_ _

The Lord Edward

23 Christchurch Place, Dublin 8
(1) 454 2158
ledward@indigo.ie
www.lordedward.ie
A famous Victorian tavern, established in 1890 and named after Lord Edward Fitzgerald, Irish aristocrat and revolutionary. It was known as Thomas Cunniam's Tavern many years ago. The pub has traded as The Lord Edward since 1967. Its restaurant is well known for its seafood.

_ _/_ _/20_ _

The Lower Deck

33 Richmond Row, Portobello, Dublin 8
(1) 475 1423
Ryan's The Lower Deck is a traditional local pub in the Portobello Harbour on the Grand Canal. My late father, Con Moloney, served his time as a barman here in the 1950s. The pub was established in 1867. A light snack menu is served and there is regular entertainment.

_ _/_ _/20_ _

Lowe's

27 Dolphins Barn Street, Dolphins Barn, Dublin 8
(1) 453 2843
A traditional local pub situated near The Coombe Hospital. It was previously called Hunt's. A light snack menu is served.

_ _/_ _/20_ _

The Malt House

27–28 James's Street, Dublin 8
A traditional local Liberties pub, established in 1709. It was previously called the Elm Bar and Crimmins. Under that name, the pub is featured in the 'Wandering Rocks' section of James Joyce's *Ulysses*. The pub is currently closed.

_ _/_ _/20_ _

McCauley's Rialto House

South Circular Road, Rialto, Dublin 8
(1) 473 6085
mccauleysbar@live.ie
Housed in a building that used to be a distillery this traditional local pub is also known as Rialto House. It was previously called Charlie Byrne's. Food is served every day and there is regular entertainment.

_ _/_ _/20_ _

McDowell's Richmond House

137 Emmet Road, Inchicore, Dublin 8
(1) 411 3614
Known locally as Mac's this traditional local pub, with regular entertainment, is St Patrick's FCA / Richmond Park's official pub. Until the 1960s, ladies were confined to the snug and were only served whiskey or half-pints of beer. The pub was established in 1868.

_ _/_ _/20_ _

McGruder's

17 Thomas Street, Dublin 8
Situated close to the Guinness Store House this traditional local pub was previously called The Limehouse, O'Reilly's and Nevin's. This establishment is currently closed.

_ _/_ _/20_ _

Francis McKenna's

29 Upper Clanbrassil Street, Harold's Cross, Dublin 8, (1) 454 6694
Named after a beer label found in the cellar, as seen over the front door, this traditional local pub has regular entertainment.

_ _/_ _/20_ _

The Millennium

4–5 Parkgate St, Dublin 8
(1) 679 5644
Situated near Heuston Station, this local traditional bar was previously called Nangle's and Reynold's. A light snack menu is served and there is regular entertainment.

_ _/_ _/20_ _

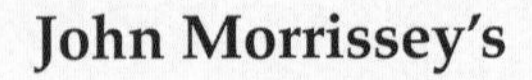

John Morrissey's

80–81 Cork Street, Dublin 8
(1) 453 3286
A traditional local pub, the last remaining bar on Cork Street, with plenty of characters. There is entertainment occasionally.

_ _/_ _/20_ _

Mother Redcap's Tavern

Back Lane, Dublin 8
A traditional pub and venue, currently closed.

_ _/_ _/20_ _

Murray's Bar

Bow Bridge House, Bow Lane West, Kilmainham, Dublin 8
(1) 707 1640
Located beside the Camac River, which can be overlooked from its balcony, this is a modern bar and lounge. Food is served every day and there is regular entertainment.

_ _/_ _/20_ _

Nancy Hands

30–32 Parkgate Street, Dublin 8, (1) 677 0149
info@nancyhands.ie, www.nancyhands.ie
A traditional bar and lounge with beautiful old timber throughout. The pub was established in 1904 andt was previously called The Deer Park. It is on The Irish Whiskey Trail and has a large selection of spirits— over 200 bottles displayed in glass cabinets behind the bar. There is an old cashier's desk behind the bar and the pub also contains an original staircase from Trinity College that featured in the film *Educating Rita*. Food is served every day and there is regular entertainment.

_ _/_ _/20_ _

Nash's

51 Patrick Street, Dublin 8
Situated near St Patrick's Cathedral on a crossroads which used to be known as 'the four corners of hell' this traditional local pub, which is currently closed, is the only remaining pub of the four that used to be on each corner of this crossroads. Two of these pubs bore the names Conway's and Lowe's.

_ _/_ _/20_ _

O'Brien's The Barn House

44–45 Dolphins Barn, Dublin 8
(1) 453 3744
A traditional local pub previously called O'Shea's Barn House and Willie Freehill's. It is known for its association with the murdered Tom Nevin, who worked as a bar manager here when his uncle owned the pub. Tom Nevin's wife, Catherine, known as 'the Black Widow', was convicted of his murder.

_ _/_ _/20_ _

The Old Harbour

6 Echlin Street, Dublin 8
A traditional family-run local pub situated near Guinness's Brewery. It was previously called The Harbour Lights. The pub was established in 1894 as a bar and grocer and has been run by the Harkins since 1992. Food is served every day and there is entertainment.

_ _/_ _/20_ _

The Old Royal Oak

Kilmanham Lane, Kilmainham, Dublin 8, (1) 671 3967
A traditional local bar and snug, established in 1874. This pub has lots of character. There is no formal scheduled entertainment, but you may catch a singalong at any time.

_ _/_ _/20_ _

O'Shea's The Merchant

O'Shea's Merchant Hotel, 12 Lower Bridge Street, Dublin 8, (1) 679 3797
info@themerchanttemplebar.com
www.themerchanttemplebar.com
A traditional Irish music bar in O'Shea's Merchant Hotel— 'The Home of Irish Music.' It is a sister hotel to O'Shea's in Talbot Street. Food is served every day and there is entertainment every night.

_ _/_ _/20_ _

The Patriots' Inn

760 South Circular Road, Kilmainham, Dublin 8
(1) 679 9595
vstapelton@patriots.com, www.patriotsinn.com
Established in 1792, this is a traditional local pub situated near Kilmainham Gaol and IMMA (the Irish Museum of Modern Art). The pub calls itself 'The home of Dublin darts' and boasts of having three men's darts teams and one women's team, so bring your arrows! Food is served most days and there is regular entertainment.

_ _/_ _/20_ _

Pifko

41–43 Usher's Quay, Dublin 8, (1) 515 2087
info@pifkobar.com, www.pifkobar.com
A traditional Irish pub, previously called The Deaf Judge, now trading as an Irish-Czech bar and restaurant. 'Pifko' is Czech for 'pint'. A pub called the Liffey Wharf once stood on a site near here. Food is served every day and there is regular entertainment.

_ _/_ _/20_ _

The Pimlico Tavern

61 Pimlico, Dublin 8
(1) 453 0867
Known locally as The Tavern this traditional local pub was completely rebuilt after the building was destroyed in 1988. A light snack menu is served and there is regular entertainment.

_ _/_ _/20_ _

Ryan's

117 James's Street, Dublin 8
There is always a great crowd in this traditional local pub, very much into sport— it is a small space well filled. It was previously called The Eagle Tavern and Paddy Hannan's, and the signage outside the pub bears this name. The pub was established circa 1750. There is regular entertainment.

_ _/_ _/20_ _

Ryan's

28 Parkgate Street, Dublin 8
(1) 677 6097
ryans@fxbrestaurants.com
www.fxbrestaurants.com
One of Dublin's best-kept original Victorian pubs, established in 1896 and locally known as Bongo's (after Bongo Ryan, a previous owner). Food is served every day. The pub is also home to the FXB Steak and Seafood Grill upstairs. If you look behind the bar, you will see an old cashiers' office.

_ _/_ _/20_ _

Ryan's

92 Lower Camden Street, Dublin 8
(1) 475 3528
Very much 'the country pub in the city' this traditional bar was previously called Sinnott's and has traded as Ryan's since the mid-1970s. The pub was established in 1882. Lunch is served on weekdays and there is regular entertainment.

_ _/_ _/20_ _

Scholar's Bar

Donovans Lane/Clanbrassil Street, Dublin 8
A traditional local pub and venue, currently closed.

_ _/_ _/20_ _

Shanahan's

25 The Coombe, Dublin 8
(1) 454 6921
A traditional local Liberties pub full of real characters. It was previously called Grumpy Jack's and The Cosy Bar. It was established in 1870.

_ _/_ _/20_ _

Slatt's

126a Tyrconnell Park, Inchicore, Dublin 8
Established in 1959 this traditional local pub is hidden away in a housing estate and is known locally as The Hideaway.

_ _/_ _/20_ _

Sure Bar

Radisson Blu Hotel, Golden Lane, Dublin 8
(1) 898 2900
info.royaldublin@radissonsblu.com
www.radissonblu.ie
A contemporary hotel bar where food is served every day. The hotel also houses the Brasserie De Verres En Vers and two private function areas, O Bar, a comfortable circular bar, and The Vintage Room, where vintage whiskey, spirits, wines and champagnes are served.

_ _/_ _/20_ _

The Tenters

1 Mill Street/Blackpitts, Dublin 8
A traditional local pub, currently closed. During the Middle Ages, victims of the bubonic plague were buried in mass graves in this area, which is still known as 'Blackpitts'.

_ _/_ _/20_ _

The Thomas House

86 Thomas Street, Dublin 8
A music bar and venue. It is often referred to as a 'dive bar', a pub which has a relaxed and informal atmosphere.

_ _/_ _/20_ _

Timothy Crough's

Emmet Road, Inchicore, Dublin 8
(1) 473 6468
A traditional local lounge bar with regular entertainment. It is built on a site where a pub called Ward's once stood.

_ _/_ _/20_ _

Tom Tavey

118 Emmet Road, Inchicore, Dublin 8
A traditional local pub with regular entertainment.
It was previously called The Pebble Mill.

_ _/_ _/20_ _

The Tram

131 James's Street, Dublin 8
A traditional local pub, previously called The Gate, The Keg and Younge's. This pub is currently closed.

_ _/_ _/20_ _

The Village Inn

Gratten Terrace, Inchicore, Dublin 8
Previously called The Emmet House this is a traditional local pub with regular entertainment.

_ _/_ _/20_ _

Chasers Lounge

308 Ballyfermot Road,
Ballyfermot, Dublin 10
(1) 626 5124
A traditional lounge on the first floor, above local shops. When the bar was located on the ground floor, it was known as Hardy's. Food is served on weekdays and there is regular entertainment.

_ _/_ _/20_ _

Cleary's Inchicore

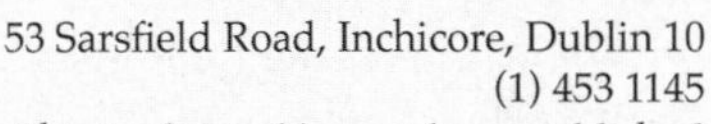

53 Sarsfield Road, Inchicore, Dublin 10
(1) 453 1145
This traditional lounge bar, established in 1820, was called Paddy Murphy's for a short time a few years ago and then reverted back to Cleary's. It has a second name—The Great Southern and Western Railway House. It is a good place to watch sports and has many sports pictures around the bar. A light snack menu is served and there is regular entertainment.

_ _/_ _/20_ _

Downey's

343 Ballyfermot Road, Ballyfermot, Dublin 10
(1) 626 4679
downeys@yahoo.ie
A traditional local pub, established in 1952. Finbarr Furey, now a local, once played here and occasionally pops in for a drink. A light snack menu is served and there is regular entertainment.

_ _/_ _/20_ _

Decies County Platform One

49 Decies Road, Ballyfermot, Dublin 10
(1) 626 5019
deciescounty@eircom.net
Founded in 1965 this is a traditional local pub with regular entertainment.

_ _/_ _/20_ _

The Laurence Lounge

7–9 Ballyfermot Road, Ballyfermot, Dublin 10
A traditional local pub with regular entertainment. It was rebuilt in 2006.

_ _/_ _/20_ _

O'Shea's

79 Ballyfermot Road, Ballyfermot, Dublin 10
(1) 626 4994
Known locally as The 79er this traditional pub was previously called The Hunting Lodge and Nalty's. Tom and Catherine Nevin worked here at one time. Food is served and there is regular entertainment.

_ _/_ _/20_ _

Ruby Finnegan's

1 First Avenue, Ballyfermot, Dublin 10
This traditional local pub was previously called The Pine Tree and is still called by this name locally. There is regular entertainment.

_ _/_ _/20_ _

Tim Younge's

203 Le Fanu Road, Ballyfermot, Dublin 10
timyoungs@yahoo.ie
A traditional local pub and music venue previously called The Lawns. A section of the pub is called Live @ Tim Youngs. A light snack menu is served and there is regular entertainment.

_ _/_ _/20_ _

The Blackforge Inn

163–165 Drimnagh Road, Drimnagh, Dublin 12
(1) 455 7860
A traditional local pub. It was previously called The Bentley and McCann's, and for three days only it was called The Old Triangle. This pub was established circa 1940. Food is served every day and there is regular entertainment.

_ _/_ _/20_ _

The Black Horse Inn (Downey's)

23 Ravensdale Park, Kimmage, Dublin 12
(1) 490 9184
A traditional local pub with regular entertainment, established in 1952.

_ _/_ _/20_ _

The Bridge House

18 Crumlin Road, Crumlin, Dublin 12
A traditional local pub by the Grand Canal. It is situated near the Camac Bridge which dates back to 1791, and has regular entertainment.

_ _/_ _/20_ _

The Cherry Tree

Walkinstown Cross, Walkinstown, Dublin 12
(1) 450 3983
A traditional local pub with regular entertainment, established in 1952. There is a music venue upstairs. 'Your local . . . You're welcome . . .' The pub was established in 1952.

_ _/_ _/20_ _

The Cottage Inn

Bluebell Avenue, Bluebell, Dublin 12
(1) 450 5111
A traditional local pub, established in 1973. Food is served on weekdays and there is regular entertainment.

_ _/_ _/20_ _

Crough's K.C.R. House

326–328 Lower Kimmage Road, Dublin 12
(1) 490 2530
K.C.R. is short for Kimmage Cross Roads. This is a traditional local pub with regular entertainment, established in 1860. The pub hosts a charity music festival every August. It may have been called The Cuman Inn at one time.

_ _/_ _/20_ _

Dillon's The Gate Bar

153–155 Crumlin Road, Crumlin, Dublin 12, (1) 454 0413
dillonspubs.info@gmail.com, www.dillonspubs.info
A traditional local pub named after St James's Gate Brewery. There are old Guinness bottles and memorabilia throughout the house, as well as one room dedicated to the writers of Dublin. This pub was established in 1946. Food is served every day except Saturday and there is regular entertainment.

_ _/_ _/20_ _

Eleanora's

147–149 Drimnagh Road, Drimnagh, Dublin 12, (1) 455 7928
A traditional local pub, previously called Downey's and Val Hatton's. It houses the Turrets Restaurant. The pub was named after Lady Eleanora of nearby Drimnagh Castle. She is rumoured to have thrown herself from the tower, and to haunt the castle to this day. The castle, which is Norman and the only castle in Ireland with a flooded moat, is open to the public in summer months. Food is served in the pub every day and there is regular entertainment.

_ _/_ _/20_ _

Freehill's Tavern

64 Saint Agnes Park, Crumlin, Dublin 12
(1) 455 5391
A traditional local pub with entertainment, established around 1940. It was previously called The Anchor, Kennedy's and The Silver Crest.

_ _/_ _/20_ _

The Halfway House

Walkinstown Road, Walkinstown, Dublin 12
(1) 429 8518
A traditional local pub. Food is served every day and there is regular entertainment.

_ _/_ _/20_ _

The Hub

St Agnew's Road, Crumlin, Dublin 12
(1) 455 5233
A traditional local pub, previously called Mooney's, Ryan's and The Shaw Arms. Food is served every day and there is regular entertainment.

_ _/_ _/20_ _

B. Hughes & Sons The Pines

196 Whitehall Road, Terenure, Dublin 12
(1) 450 4162
thepines@eircom.net
A traditional local pub established in 1953. Food is served every day and there is regular entertainment.

_ _/_ _/20_ _

McGowan's Kestrel Inn

Walkinstown Road / Cross, Walkinstown, Dublin 12
(01) 4508 555
A traditional local landmark pub. When first built it was in the middle of the roundabout! This pub was previously called The Parkway Inn and The Kestrel House. Food is served every day and there is regular entertainment.

_ _/_ _/20_ _

Kylemore House

Kylemore Road, Bluebell, Dublin 12
A traditional local pub, currently closed.

_ _/_ _/20_ _

The Laurels (Hughes')

186 West Whitehall Road, Perrystown, Dublin 12
(1) 450 4270
A traditional local pub established in 1963. Food is served every day and there is regular entertainment.

_ _/_ _/20_ _

The Longmile Inn

4 Long Mile Road, Drimnagh, Dublin 12
(1) 450 3138
A traditional local pub. It was previously called Slattery's. Food is served every day and there is regular entertainment.

_ _/_ _/20_ _

Marble Arch (Fitzgerald's)

1 Benbulbin Road, Drimnagh, Dublin 12
(1) 409 9506
www.louisfitzgerald.com
Fitzgerald's Marble Arch is a traditional local pub along the Grand Canal and opposite the Golden Bridge Luas station. It was previously called The White Horse Inn. There is regular entertainment.

_ _/_ _/20_ _

Mini McCabe's Bar

Sheldon Park Hotel, Kylemore Road,
Kylemore/Bluebell, Dublin 12
(1) 460 1055
info@sheldonpark.ie
www.sheldonpark.ie
Hotel bar of The Sheldon Park Hotel. Food is served every day and there is regular entertainment. The hotel, which is also home to Heuston's Restaurant, was established in 1996.

_ _/_ _/20_ _

Murray's The Four Roads

140–142 Sundrive Road, Kimmage/Crumlin, Dublin 12
(1) 454 2463
A traditional local pub with regular entertainment. It was previously called Hanrahan's Four Roads. A light snack menu is served.

_ _/_ _/20_ _

The Old County

125–127 Old County Road, Crumlin, Dublin 12
(1) 455 6622
Established circa 1950 this traditional local pub first opened as The County Bar and later was called The Ivy Leaf and The Fair Exchange.

_ _/_ _/20_ _

Quinn's

14 St Agnes Road, Crumlin, Dublin 12
Established circa 1950 this traditional local pub was called The Horseshoe Inn up to 2011. It is currently closed.

_ _/_ _/20_ _

Rueben's Café Bar

The Aspect Hotel, Park West Business Campus, Nangor Road, Clondalkin, Dublin 12, (1) 642 9100
info@aspecthotelparkwest.com
www.aspecthotelparkwest.com
A modern café bar in The Aspect Hotel. The hotel was previously called Day's Hotel.

_ _/_ _/20_ _

Sheary's

3 Bangor Drive (off Crumlin Rd), Crumlin, Dublin 12
(1) 453 1381
A traditional local pub established in 1962 by Kevin Vaughan and Pat Sheary. The two good friends called the pub The Good Companions. It has traded as Sheary's since 1989.

_ _/_ _/20_ _

The Stoneboat

35 Sundrive Road, Kimmage, Dublin 12, (1) 492 1794
A traditional local pub which boasts of having had Christy Brown as a punter in the past. It was previously called Davy Brennan's, Fisher's, Jim Leigh's, Summer's, and The Turk's Head. I am told it took its present name from a stone on a sandbank in the nearby river Poddle which was in the shape of a boat. Locals call the pub 'The Boat'. The pub was established in 1896. A light snack menu is served on weekdays.

_ _/_ _/20_ _

The Submarine

Cromwellsfort Road, Crumlin Cross, Kimmage, Dublin 12
(1) 455 6074
Known locally as The Sub, this is a traditional local pub, 'Dublin's home of darts.' One of the bars is called Rory O'Connor's Bar, named after a well-known local Irish dancer. The pub also houses The Whitehall Room, which is mainly used for functions. The pub was established in 1947. It was completely rebuilt in the early 1990s and the sub-lounge is now a wide open space designed to look like a theatre. There are seated areas to either side, which staff call 'The Muppet Boxes'. The room also has lighting over a large stage, mostly used for live bands. Food is served every day and there is entertainment most nights.

_ _/_ _/20_ _

The Whitefriar

Cashel Road, Kimmage, Dublin 12
A traditional local pub built from old salvaged timbers. It was established in 2006. This pub is currently closed.

_ _/_ _/20_ _

The Traders

Limekiln Green, St James's Road,
Walkinstown, Dublin 12
(1) 450 9901
www.louisfitzgerald.com
A traditional local pub established in 1973 by Paddy Belton. Food is served on weekdays and there is regular entertainment.

_ _/_ _/20_ _

The Village Inn

24 Lisle Road, Crumlin, Dublin 12
(1) 455 7861
thevillageinnd12@eircom.net
A traditional local pub with regular entertainment. A light snack menu is served.

_ _/_ _/20_ _

The Bottle Tower

1 Beaumont Avenue, Churchtown, Dublin 14
A traditional local pub named after the Bottle Tower in Churchtown, a folly built in the severely cold winter of 1741–42 as relief work for the poor. The pub was established in 1962 and is also called Ned Finnegan's. A light snack menu is served.

_ _/_ _/20_ _

The Castle Inn

39 Main Street, Rathfarnham, Dublin 14
(1) 490 6866
thecastleinn@eircom.net
www.thecastleinn.info
A traditional local pub run by the Donnellans since circa 1968. Food is served every day and there is regular entertainment.

_ _/_ _/20_ _

The Eagle

Main Street, Dundrum, Dublin 14
(1) 298 1572
A traditional local pub with regular entertainment, also home to The Nest Lounge. The pub is located just two minutes' walk from Dundrum Town Centre.

_ _/_ _/20_ _

The Glenside

Landscape Road, Churchtown, Dublin 14
(1) 298 5932
A traditional local pub with a thatched roof. Food is served every day and there is regular entertainment. The Arch Bistro is connected to the pub and is situated on the upper level. The pub was established in 1950.

_ _/_ _/20_ _

The Goat

Taney Road, Goatstown Cross, Goatstown, Dublin 14
(1) 298 4145
info@goatgrill.com
www.goatgrill.com
A traditional local sports bar with regular entertainment. The Goat Bar features collected memorabilia from the sporting world. The pub, which is also home to The Stirrups Restaurant, was established in 1741 and was first licensed in 1792. Food is served every day.

_ _/_ _/20_ _

Corner House

9 Windy Arbour Dundrum Road, Dundrum, Dublin 14
A traditional local pub. It was previously called JD's Corner House, Kyne's Corner House, The Millrace, and The Nine Arches.

_ _/_ _/20_ _

The Old Orchard Inn

Butterfield Avenue, Rathfarnham, Dublin 14
(1) 494 3803
theoldorchardinn@gmail.com
www.theoldorchardinn.ie
A traditional local pub with regular entertainment. It is locally known as The Thrippeny bit as it has a 360-degree circular bar. The pub was established in 1945. There are summer barbeques in the beer garden where you will find Ali's Bar.

_ _/_ _/20_ _

The Rathfarnham House

Rathfarnham Old Village, Rathfarnham, Dublin 14
A traditional local pub with entertainment. It is also home to XS Nightclub which opens at weekends. The pub was previously called The Rathfarnham Inn, Sarah Curran's, Seasons and Touch Nightclub.

_ _/_ _/20_ _

The Rockfield Lounge

Block 14, Rockfield Central, Dundrum, Dublin 14
(1) 296 4650
johndapnekearney@hotmail.com
A lounge bar situated near Balally Luas station. It was established in 2005. Food is served every day and there is regular entertainment.

_ _/_ _/20_ _

The Revels

37 Main Street, Rathfarnham, Dublin 14
(1) 490 1376
A traditional local pub, with entertainment occasionally.

_ _/_ _/20_ _

Rodeo Joe's Bar and Club

Upper Churchtown Road, Churchtown, Dublin 14
A bar and club, previously called The Braemor Rooms and McGowan's Pub. This establishment is currently closed.

_ _/_ _/20_ _

Ruairi Maguire's

Dundrum Town Centre, Ballinteer Road, Dundrum, Dublin 14
A traditional Irish-style gastro pub founded in 2009. This establishment is currently closed.

_ _/_ _/20_ _

Ryan's Dundrum House

57 Main Street, Dundrum, Dublin 14, (1) 296 1097
A traditional local pub, locally known as The DH. It was previously called McCann's, Murphy's and The Swallow, and has traded as Ryan's since the early 1960s. Food is served every day and there is entertainment on the first Saturday of the month.

_ _/_ _/20_ _

Ryan's Arbour House

Windy Arbour, Dundrum Road, Dundrum, Dublin 14
(1) 298 4372
A traditional local pub with regular entertainment situated near Windy Arbour Luas station. The bar is called The Riverside Bar. The pub was established in 1899.

_ _/_ _/20_ _

TGI Friday's

Dundrum Shopping Centre, Dublin 14
(1) 298 7299
dundrum@fridays.ie
www.fridays.ie
Situated on the first floor of the Dundrum Town Centre this is a branch of the American restaurant and bar chain. 'In here, it's always Friday'. The interior is filled with various kinds of automobile, musical and sports memorabilia.

_ _/_ _/20_ _

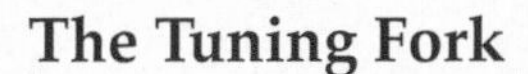

The Tuning Fork

Whitechurch Road, Rathfarnham, Dublin 14
A traditional local pub, established in 1907. It is currently closed.

_ _/_ _/20_ _

Uncle Tom's Cabin

Rosemount, Dundrum, Dublin 14
(1) 298 4357
A traditional local pub which also bears the name James Collins. The pub was established in 1878. Food is served every day.

_ _/_ _/20_ _

The Yellow House

1 Willowbrook Road, Rathfarnham, Dublin 14
(1) 493 2994
This traditional local pub and landmark is named after the yellow brick from which it was built in 1825. The brick came from an old inn, dating back to the 18th century, which was situated on the opposite side of the road. Food is served every day. I am told Finbar Furey often pops in for a drink. The pub is also home to Morille's Restaurant on the first floor.

_ _/_ _/20_ _

The Balally Inn

Sandyford Shopping Centre, Balally, Dublin 16
(1) 295 2787
Known locally as 'The Inn' this is a traditional local pub with a pool and snooker room. The pub was established around 1970.

_ _/_ _/20_ _

The Ballinteer House

Ballinteer Shopping Centre, Ballinteer Avenue, Ballinteer, Dublin 16
(1) 295 1183
A traditional local pub with a snooker room. It was established in 1977 and is known locally as 'The BH'. It was previously called The Beavers Pub. Food is served every day.

_ _/_ _/20_ _

The Blue Haven

1 Ballyroan Road, Rathfarnham, Dublin 16
(1) 494 5382
A traditional bar and lounge.

__/__/20__

Bugler's Ballyboden House

Ballyboden Road, Rathfarnham, Dublin 16
(1) 493 2358
A traditional local pub with entertainment, established in 1798. A light snack menu is served.

__/__/20__

The Coach House

Ballinteer Avenue, Ballinteer, Dublin 16
(1) 298 7088
A traditional local pub with occasional entertainment. Food is served every day.

__/__/20__

M. J. Delany's

Knocklyon, Templeogue, Dublin 16
(1) 494 7161
Delany's Knocklyon Inn is a traditional pub situated right beside the M50 motorway. It was established as a bar and grocer in 1842. There is a great gallery of historic pictures throughout the house. A light snack menu is served and there is regular entertainment.

__/__/20__

The Eden House

Grange Road, Rathfarnham, Dublin 16, (1) 493 1492
suzannelawless@eircom.net, www.edenhouse.ie
This country pub was opened in 1976 in a Victorian manor house, built in 1863. The setting is lovely, with the pub divided into The Drawing Room, The Library Room, The Garden of Eden Smoking Area, The Music Room, The Racing Room and The Snug. Food is served every day and there is regular entertainment.

_ _/_ _/20_ _

The Furry Bog

Whitechurch Green, Rathfarnham, Dublin 16
(1) 495 2507
furrybogaccount@hotmail.com
www.thefurrybog.com
A traditional local pub established in 1985. Food is served every day and there is regular entertainment.

_ _/_ _/20_ _

The Merry Ploughboy

Rockbrook, Edmondstown Road, Rathfarnham, Dublin 16
(1) 493 1495
info@mpb.com, www.mpbpub.com
A traditional pub and venue, originally established in 1780, and now owned and run by traditional musicians. The pub holds traditional dinners and shows nightly which feature Irish dance, music and song all year round. The pub also has a shuttle bus service to the city centre.

_ _/_ _/20_ _

Taylor's Three Rock

Grange Road, Rathfarnham, Dublin 16, (1) 494 2311
info@taylorsthreerock.ie, www.taylorsthreerock.ie
Formerly a farmhouse where the Taylor family lived, this is now a traditional local pub and Irish cabaret venue. The bar is called The Farmhouse Bar. An Irish Nights entertainment show is held every night all year round, and every night from May to October there is an Irish cabaret show. The pub has traded as Taylor's Three Rock since 1973. Food is served every day.

_ _/_ _/20_ _

The Willows/Macker's Bar

26–28 Willow Road, Ballinteer / Dundrum, Dublin 16
(1) 298 4310
A traditional local pub established in 1960 and known locally as Macker's. There is a snooker room on the upper level.

_ _/_ _/20_ _

Winters

Sandyford Road, Dundrum, Dublin 16
(1) 216 6848
info@winters.ie
www.winters.ie
A modern local bar and restaurant and home to Parker Brown's nightclub. The nightclub is open Thursday to Sunday. The pub was established in 2005. Bar food is served every day and there is regular entertainment.

_ _/_ _/20_ _

Bewley's Hotel Bar

Bewley's Hotel, Central Park, Leopardstown, Dublin 18
(1) 293 5000
leopardstown@bewleyshotels.com
www.bewleyshotels.com
A hotel bar and brasserie situated near Leopardstown Racecourse. It is used mainly for conference and business meetings. Food is served in the bar every day.

_ _/_ _/20_ _

The Blue Light

Barnacullia, Sandyford, Dublin 18
(1) 216 0487
This traditional rustic-style pub has real turf fires in winter. It is situated in the Dublin Mountains and its seating area outside has stunning views of Dublin. There is regular entertainment.

_ _/_ _/20_ _

Crystal Bar

Beacon Court Boutique Hotel, Beacon Court,
Sandyford Business Region, Sandyford, Dublin 18
(1) 291 5000
reservations@thebeacon.com
www.thebeacon.com
This candlelit hotel bar has a very relaxing contemporary feel. Food is served in the bar every day. The hotel is also home to the My Thai restaurant.

_ _/_ _/20_ _

Fillies Café Bar

Leopardstown Racecourse, Leopardstown, Dublin 18
(1) 289 8852
fillies@iol.ie
www.club92.ie
A bar in the centre of Leopardstown Racecourse complex. Food is served every day and there is occasional entertainment. Fillies is connected to Club 92 which was previously called Blinkers and Papillon.

_ _/_ _/20_ _

The Gallops

Ballyogan Road, Leopardstown, Dublin 18
(1) 294 2401
A traditional local sports pub with horseracing memorabilia throughout the house. Part of the bar is called Lester's Bar. This pub was established in 1996.

_ _/_ _/20_ _

The Horse and Hound (Brennan's)

Cabinteely, Dublin 18
(1) 285 3527
A traditional local pub, established circa 1950. Food is served every day and there is regular entertainment.

_ _/_ _/20_ _

Lamb Doyle's Steakhouse and Grill

Blackglen Road, Sandyford, Dublin 18
(1) 295 9592
info@lambdoyles.com
www.lambdoyles.com
Situated in the foothills of the Dublin Mountains this traditional local pub has great views of the south of the city and Dun Laoghaire harbour. It was once known as Lamb Doyle's Roadhouse. Food is served every day.

_ _/_ _/20_ _

Madigan's

Leopardstown Racecourse, Leopardstown, Dublin 18
pubs@madigan.ie
www.madigan.ie
This traditional pub opens only when race meetings or events are taking place.

_ _/_ _/20_ _

The Magic Carpet

Cornelscourt Village, Cornelscourt, Dublin 18
(1) 289 7257
At one time this traditional local pub was a famous music venue. It was previously called Connolly's. Food is served on weekdays and there is occasional entertainment.

_ _/_ _/20_ _

The Sandyford House

Sandyford Village, Sandyford, Dublin 18
(1) 295 4615
www.sandyfordhouse.ie
Walsh's Sandyford House is a family-run traditional local pub with regular entertainment. Food is served every day. It is also home to La Dolce Vita Restaurant on the first floor. There are many different sections to the bar, including Ma Flavin's Bar, Michael's Lean To, and The Sitting Room. The pub was established in 1607 as a bar and grocer shop and has traded as Walsh's since around 1910.

_ _/_ _/20_ _

The Step Inn

Stepaside Village, Dublin 18
(1) 295 6202
info@thestepinn.com
www.thestepinn.com
A traditional local gastro pub located at the foot of the Dublin Mountains. The pub also houses The Stone Grill restaurant, which is famous for its steaks. The pub was established circa 1900 and was previously called Barry Kavanagh's. There is regular entertainment.

_ _/_ _/20_ _

The Turf Club Bar

Stillorgan Park Hotel, Stillorgan Road, Stillorgan, Dublin 18
(1) 200 1800
sales@stillorganpark.com
www.stillorganpark.com
A traditional hotel bar. Food is served every day, and there is regular entertainment. The hotel also houses The Purple Sage Restaurant.

_ _/_ _/20_ _

The Angler's Rest

Knockmaroon Hill, Strawberry Beds, Chapelizod, Dublin 20, (1) 820 4351
info@theanglersrest.ie, www.theanglersrest.ie
Gilbert Wright's Angler's Rest is a traditional Irish gastro-pub and seafood restaurant, originally established in 1862. The main bar is called The Salmon Bar. The pub was used as a location for part of the film *Hear My Song*, a biopic about the renowned singer Josef Locke. There is regular entertainment.

_ _/_ _/20_ _

The Bridge Inn

1 Saint Laurence's Road, Chapelizod, Dublin 20
(1) 620 6747
A traditional local pub established in 1911 and run by the Kavanagh family— 'Dublin City's only pub that actually sits on the River Liffey'. It is named after Chapelizod Bridge, which was re-named The Anna Livia Bridge in 1982. The pub was previously called Dillon's, Galligan's, Murray's, Ryan's and Shelvin's. Food is served every day and there is regular entertainment.

_ _/_ _/20_ _

The Deadman's Bar and Dining

Old Lucan Road, Curtis Stream, Palmerstown,
Dublin 20, (1) 626 5466
info@deadmansinn.com, www.deadmansinn.com
The Deadman's Bar and Dining is a traditional local pub serving food every day and with regular entertainment. It is also home to Club 3 Zero. The pub, which is just off The M4 motorway, was previously called Murray's, O'Connells Inn and most recently The Deadman's Inn. It was established in 1702 and got its name from an incident in 1789 when a coachmen fell off the coach outside Murray's Inn and died. Locals laid him out in the inn and arranged his burial.

_ _/_ _/20_ _

The Liffey Bar

West County Hotel, Chapelizod Road,
Chapelizod, Dublin 20
(1) 626 4011
info@westcountyhotel.ie
www.westcountyhotel.ie
A hotel bar housed within the family-run West County Hotel. Food is served every day and there is regular entertainment. The hotel, which was established around 1970, also houses The Pine Restaurant.

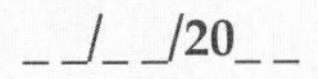

_ _/_ _/20_ _

The Mullingar House

DUBLIN AND EAST TOURISM
HOME OF ALL CHARACTERS AND ELEMENTS IN JAMES JOYCE'S NOVEL "FINNEGANS WAKE"

Chapelizod Village, Dublin 20, (1) 620 8692
Home to all the characters in James Joyce's novel, *Finnegans Wake* this traditional local pub was established in 1694. It also houses The Patriots' Rest Restaurant'. Food is served in the bar every day and there is regular entertainment.

_ _/_ _/20_ _

The Palmerstown House

Old Lucan Road, Palmerstown Village, Dublin 20
(1) 626 4505
palmerstownhouse@fitzgeraldgroup.ie
www.louisfitzgeraldgroup.ie
Considered to be one of Dublin's more historic coach houses this traditional local pub was established in 1732. It is often referred to by its previous name, The Black Swan, or the nickname The Mucky Duck. Food is served every day and there is regular entertainment.

_ _/_ _/20_ _

The Silver Granite

Kennelsfort Road, Palmerstown, Dublin 20
(1) 626 4050
www.toweygroup.com
A traditional local pub with regular entertainment, and serving a light snack menu on weekdays. It was established in 1963.

_ _/_ _/20_ _

The Strawberry Hall

Strawberry Beds, Chapelizod , Dublin 20
821 0634
A traditional local pub located along the River Liffey, well known as a bikers' stop-off. They play bagatelle here—a table game similar to billiards.

_ _/_ _/20_ _

The Villager

31 Main Street, Chapelizod, Dublin 20
(1) 626 1766
A traditional local pub established in 1894, previously called A Peat's and The Tap. There is a bar upstairs called The Tap Bar. A light snack menu is served in the bar every day and there is regular entertainment.

_ _/_ _/20_ _

The Wren's Nest

Strawberry Beds, Chapelizod, Dublin 20
A traditional local pub along the banks of the River Liffey, run by the same family for five generations. This is the only pub I have visited in Dublin that has a fireplace behind the bar. It was established in 1855.

_ _/_ _/20_ _

The Arc Café Bar

Liffey Valley Shopping Centre, Fonthill Road, Clondalkin, Dublin 22
(1) 620 7003
info@arcbar.net
www.arcbar.net
Described as 'a premier state-of-the-art venue and restaurant' close to Liffey Valley Shopping Centre. It was established in 2002. Food is served every day and there is regular entertainment.

_ _/_ _/20_ _

Bewley's Hotel

Bewley's Hotel, Newlands Cross, Naas Road, Clondalkin, Dublin 22, 4640140
newlandscross@bewleyshotels.com, www.bewleyshotels.com
A hotel bar and brasserie popular with people travelling to and from the south on the N7 who want to be located near the city centre. The hotel facilities are also used for conference and business meetings.

_ _/_ _/20_ _

Boomers Bar

Dutch Village Shopping Centre, Woodford Walk, Clondalkin, Dublin 22, (1) 464 1018
boomers@eircom.net, www.rorysbistro.ie
Boomer's is a traditional local family-run pub, established in 1995. It also bears the name Brugha's. Food is served in the bar every day and there is regular entertainment. Boomers are renowned for darts playing. They are also home to Rory's Bistro on the upper floor.

_ _/_ _/20_ _

Brown's Barn

Citywest Bridge, Naas Road (N7), Clondalkin, Dublin 22
(1) 464 0999
www.brownsbarn.net
A modern bar, also called Silken Thomas, in a historic building which housed the Royal Garters Stables in the 18th century. In 1815 the building served as Bianconi's principal depot when he set up his coaching service which transformed transport in Ireland. Food is served in the bar every day and there is regular entertainment.

_ _/_ _/20_ _

Finches

Neilstown Road, Clondalkin, Dublin 22
(1) 626 3712
finches@fitzgeraldgroup.ie
www.louisfitzgerald.com
A traditional local pub with regular entertainment, previously called Belton's.

_ _/_ _/20_ _

Fowlers Grange Cross

Le Fanu Road, Ballyfermot, Dublin 22
(1) 626 4927
A traditional local pub previously called The County Bar. Food is served every day and there is regular entertainment.

_ _/_ _/20_ _

The Grill Room

Maldron Hotel, Kingswood Village, Naas Road, Dublin 22
(1) 464 2732
info@thegrillroom.ie info.citywest@maldronhotels.com
www.thegrillroom.ie www.maldronhotels.com
A steakhouse and bar set in Kingswood House, in the grounds of The Maldron Hotel complex. Kingswood House, which dates dack to around 1730, was once the home of the renowned Irish tenor, Josef Locke. Its previous names were Josef's and The Kingswood House Bar and Grill. The Maldron Hotel is home to Stir Café Bar which is mainly used by residents. This hotel was previously called The Comfort Inn.

_ _/_ _/20_ _

Hannigen's in the Plaza

Block 71, The Plaza, Clondalkin, Dublin 22
The Plaza is Clondalkin's business centre. Hannigen's is currently closed. Its previous name was Bennigans and for a short time before it closed it traded as Q Venue.

_ _/_ _/20_ _

ibis Hotel Cafe

ibis Hotel, Monastery Road, Clondalkin, Dublin 22
(1) 464 1480
h0595@accor.com
www.ibishotel.com
Situated in the ibis Hotel near the Red Cow roundabout off the N7 motorway, this bar is mostly used by residents.

_ _/_ _/20_ _

Joel's Restaurant

Naas Road N7, Newlands Cross, Dublin 22
(1) 459 2968
joelsrestaurant@fitzgeraldgroup.ie, www.joels.ie
A large family restaurant and party venue, including The Dispense Bar. It has lots of entertainment for children. Joel's is connected to The Louis Fitzgerald Hotel. Originally established in 1991, it was demolished in 1997 and rebuilt in less than three months.

_ _/_ _/20_ _

Kudos

Clarion Hotel, Liffey Valley Complex, Liffey Valley, Dublin 22
(1) 625 8000
kudos@clarionhotelliffeyvalley.com
www.clariondublinliffeyvalley.com
Hotel bar of The Clarion Hotel. Food is served every day and there is regular entertainment. The hotel also houses The Sinergie Restaurant and Savour Lounge.

_ _/_ _/20_ _

The Laurels

Main Street, Clondalkin Village, Dublin 22
(1) 457 0833
laurels@louisfitzgeraldgroup.ie
www.louisfitzgerald.com
A modern meets traditional pub. It has a back bar fitting that originally came from a hotel in Chicago where Al Capone ran his business. Food is served every day and there is regular entertainment.

_ _/_ _/20_ _

LJ's Bar and Restaurant

Louis Fitzgerald Hotel, Naas Road, Newlands Cross, Dublin 22
(1) 403 3300
stay@louisfitzgeraldhotel.com, www.louisfitzgeraldhotel.com
A very modern bar and restaurant in The Louis Fitzgerald Hotel, which was established in 2007. There are great paintings in the lobby as well as a 1904 Vintage Wolseley Car. It is interconnected to Joel's Restaurant. Food is served every day and there is regular entertainment.

_ _/_ _/20_ _

Quinlan's The Black Lion

Orchard Road, Clondalkin Village, Dublin 22
(1) 457 0897
A traditional local pub which is also home to Q Club. Food is served every day and there is regular entertainment. The pub was established in 1838.

_ _/_ _/20_ _

The Red Cow Inn

Red Cow Complex, Naas Road, Clondalkin, Dublin 22
(1) 459 3650
redcowinfo@moranhotels.com
www.moranhotels.com www.redcowhotel.com
The Red Cow Inn Bar and Hush Nightclub are in the grounds of The Moran Red Cow Hotel. Food is served in the bar every day and there is regular entertainment. Hush Nightclub opens Friday to Sunday. The hotel is home to The Cocktail Bar and The Winter Garden Restaurant. The Red Cow complex attracts both local customers and passing trade from the nearby M50 motorway.

_ _/_ _/20_ _

Rosie O'Grady

Green Isle Hotel, Naas Road, Newlands Cross, Dublin 22, (1) 459 3406
info@greenislehotel.com, www.greenislehotel.com
Bar of the Brennan Green Isle Hotel, which also has a conference centre as well as leisure and spa facilities. It is just off the N7 motorway. Food is served every day in Rosie O'Grady's and there is regular entertainment.

_ _/_ _/20_ _

The Steering Wheel

Main Street, Clondalkin Village, Dublin 22
(1) 457 8898
A traditional local bar with a large lounge upstairs. This pub was previously called The Castle and The Store House. The pub is near Tully's Castle, a 16th-century tower. The pub was established in 1980. Food is served every day and there is regular entertainment.

_ _/_ _/20_ _

The Swallows

St Cuthbert's Road, Deansrath, Clondalkin, Dublin 22
(1) 457 6267
A traditional local pub established in 1992. Food is served every day and there is regular entertainment.

_ _/_ _/20_ _

The Village Inn

Clondalkin Village, Dublin 22
(1) 457 7070
A traditional local pub with a modern lounge and beer garden on the upper levels. It was previously called Baroque. Food is served every day and there is regular entertainment.

_ _/_ _/20_ _

The Waterside

Ninth Lock, Clondalkin, Dublin 22
(1) 457 7716
thewaterside@hotmail.com
www.watersidebar.ie
Situated along the banks of the Grand Canal at Lock 9, this traditional local pub was previously called The Lock and Quay and Palmer's, and has traded as The Waterside since 2005. It also houses Reed's function room. Food is served every day and there is regular entertainment.

_ _/_ _/20_ _

Aherne's

Old Bawn Road, Tallaght, Dublin 24
(1) 451 0438
A well-known landmark pub. This large traditional-style local is a great place to watch sports.

_ _/_ _/20_ _

Blu Bar

2 Tuansgate, The Square, Tallaght, Dublin 24
A modern bar in the Tallaght Town Centre. It was established in 2006 and also houses The Renaissance Nightclub. This establishment is currently closed.

Brady's Fortunestown Inn

Fortunestown Way, Tallaght, Dublin 24
(1) 459 9494
A traditional local pub. It was previously called Molly Heffernan's. Food is served on Sundays and there is regular entertainment.

_ _/_ _/20_ _

Captain America's

Unit A3 Tallaght Cross, Tallaght, Dublin 24
(1) 414 1426
tallaght@captainamericas.com
www.captainamericas.com
An American-style music venue, bar and restaurant, with various pieces of music memorabilia on display. Captain America's was established in Dublin in 1971. This branch opened in Tallaght in 2007. Food is served every day and there is regular entertainment.

_ _/_ _/20_ _

Crough's

Cookstown Road, off Maplewood Rd, Tallaght, Dublin 24
(1) 452 8498
A traditional local pub. Food is served every day and there is regular entertainment.

_ _/_ _/20_ _

The Cuckoo's Nest (Lynch's)

Greenhills Road, Tallaght, Dublin 24, (1) 451 5061
bernard@cuckoosnest.ie
A traditional local pub, established in 1739 and run by the Lynch family since 1962. Food is served every day and there is regular entertainment. A bar within this pub is called Peader's Bar, after the owner, Peadar Lynch. The pub is also home to The Wicked Chicken function room.

_ _/_ _/20_ _

The Dragon Inn

Main Street, Tallaght, Dublin 24
(1) 451 1472
James J. Murphy The Dragon Inn is a traditional local pub with regular entertainment. It was established in 1765.

_ _/_ _/20_ _

The Foxes' Covert

4 Main Street, Tallaght, Dublin 24
(1) 452 7965
Molloy's The Foxes Covert is a traditional 'social local' pub, established around 1800. It was a well-known cabaret venue in the 1970s. The pub has a large function room called The Fables. Food is served on weekdays and there is regular entertainment.

_ _/_ _/20_ _

Grumpy McClafferty's

Plaza Hotel, Belgard Road, Tallaght, Dublin 24, (1) 404 7444
info@plazahotel.ie, www.plazahotel.ie
Food is served in this hotel bar every day and there is occasional entertainment. The hotel also houses Vista Cafe, The Olive Tree Restaurant, and The Playhouse Nightclub, previously called O Bar and Nightclub. The hotel opened in 1999.

_ _/_ _/20_ _

Jobstown House

Blessington Road, Tallaght,
Dublin 24, (1) 459 9799
A traditional local pub, established circa 1840. A light snack menu is served and there is regular entertainment.

_ _/_ _/20_ _

Kilcawley's Bar

Abberley Court Hotel, Belgard Road/High Street, Tallaght, Dublin 24
(1) 459 6000
info@abberley.ie
www.abberley.ie
A hotel bar housed within The Abberley Court Hotel, which is also home to Level 4 Nightclub. The nightclub opens on Fridays and Saturdays. Food is served in the bar every day and there is regular entertainment.

_ _/_ _/20_ _

Killinarden House

Killinarden Road, Tallaght, Dublin 24
(1) 451 7276
A traditional local pub known locally as The Killo. The pub was established in 1980. Food is served on Saturdays and there is regular entertainment.

_ _/_ _/20_ _

Kiltipper Café Bar

Neighbourhood Centre, Marlfield Mall, Kiltipper Way, Tallaght, Dublin 24
(1) 452 0811
robkavanagh300@hotmail.com
A modern café bar established in 2006. Food is served every day and there is regular entertainment.

_ _/_ _/20_ _

The Kingswood Lodge

Ballymount Road, Tallaght, Dublin 24
(1) 451 4567
A traditional local pub, established in 1989. It was previously called The Clock Tower. Food is served every day and there is regular entertainment.

_ _/_ _/20_ _

Lannigan's Belgard Inn

Belgard Road, Tallaght, Dublin 24
(1) 414 0400
A traditional local pub and club, established in 1973, at which time it was the largest public house in Europe. There is regular entertainment. The Belgard also houses Coco's Function Room, which was formerly a nightclub, and Lannigan's Function Room.

_ _/_ _/20_ _

Metro Café Bar

Old Blessington Road, Tallaght, Dublin 24
(1) 544 6305
metrotallaght@gmail.com
A trendy cocktail bar established in 2006. Food is served every day and there is regular entertainment.

_ _/_ _/20_ _

Morton's The Firhouse Inn

Firhouse Road, Firhouse, Dublin 24
(1) 494 6361
A traditional pub, established circa 1860. 'A social local pub'. The bar is called Harry's Bar. Food is served from Wednesday to Saturday and there is regular entertainment.

_ _/_ _/20_ _

The Old Mill

Old Bawn Road, Tallaght, Dublin 24, (1) 459 6770
oldmill@fitzgeraldgroupe.ie,www.louisfitzgerald.com
A very large pub and restaurant, styled after a mill, using the contents of an old mill from Borrisokane, County Tipperary. It has numerous nooks and crannies. A mill dating from the 1750s used to stand on this site. A pub called Bridget Bourke's, which was a well-known cabaret venue, also occupied the site until it was demolished in 1997 by Louis Fitzgerald who replaced it with the current pub. Food is served every day and there is regular entertainment.

_ _/_ _/20_ _

The Penny Black Tavern

Castletymon Road, Tymon North, Tallaght, Dublin 24
(1) 452 5876
A traditional local pub established in 1987. Food is served every day and there is regular entertainment.

_ _/_ _/20_ _

Scholars

Old Court Centre, Parklands Road, Firhouse, Dublin 24
(1) 451 6757
scholarspub@eircom.net
A traditional local pub established in 2000. Food is served every day and there is regular entertainment.

_ _/_ _/20_ _

The Speaker Connolly

Firhouse Road, Firhouse, Dublin 24
(1) 452 7833
A traditional local pub named after William Connolly, who was Speaker in the Irish Parliament in the 18th century. He built the house in the Dublin Mountains which became the Hell Fire Club, and also built Castletown House. Food is served in the pub every day and there is regular entertainment.

_ _/_ _/20_ _

Stir Café Bar

The Maldron Hotel, Whitestown Way, Tallaght, Dublin 24
(1) 468 5400
info.tallaght@maldronhotels.com
www.maldronhotels.com
Café bar of The Maldron Hotel. Food is served every day. The hotel was previously called The Tower Hotel.

_ _/_ _/20_ _

The Martello Tower in Donabate, North Co Dublin

North County Dublin

The Naul, Balscadden, Balbriggan, Balrothery, Ballyboughal, Oldtown, Skerries, Lusk, Rush, Donabate, Howth, Garristown, Kinsealy, Cloghran, Swords, Malahide and Collinstown

The Naul village is on the border of Dublin and Meath. It is believed that the area has been occupied since the Stone Age.

Balscadden is just to the north of Balbriggan, and is one of the northernmost villages in Dublin. It is situated on the Belfast–Dublin main line of the Irish rail network. It has an attractive beach and harbour.

In the past the village of Balbriggan was a small fishing village. In the late eighteenth century industry came to the area, with the introduction of cotton factories. Since that time there has been much development in the area, with plans for further expansion in the near future.

Balrothery is a village located south of Balbriggan. The name Balrothery comes from the Irish Baile an Ridire, Town of the Knight.

Ballyboughal is a small town located about 12 km from Swords. It is also home to an aerodrome and a pitch-and-putt club.

Oldtown is a compact rural village, with narrow roads and village lanes around Oldtown House. Many of its existing houses were built in the nineteenth century.

Skerries was in the past a thriving fishing port and a centre for hand embroidery. It has since become a resort town, offering golf, sailing, motorcyling and other amenities. Ardgillan Castle, situated between Skerries and Balbriggan, is an imposing residence built in the eighteenth century.

Lusk, originally a small village, has undergone a large population growth over the last ten years. One of its most imposing ancient monuments is Lusk Church, part of which is a Norman Square tower.

Rush was once considered the heart of market gardening in Leinster. Nowadays Rush is better known as a commuter belt town.

Donabate, a growing suburban coastal town, is situated on a peninsula. Although Ireland's east coast is not ideal for surfing, surfers are regularly seen at Donabate beach.

Howth is located on the peninsula of Howth Head, on the north side of Dublin Bay. It is a mixture of residential development and wild hillside. The area offers spectacular cliff walks, with the Baily Lighthouse being a striking feature on the headland. Howth town has an attractive harbour and is a popular destination for tourists and locals alike.

Garristown is a small village in the north western corner of County Dublin, and is located on hilly country. Its population is still around 400 people.

Kinsealy is an outer suburb of Dublin, and is currently undergoing major developments. It was home for many years to Charles Haughey, former Taoiseach.

Cloghran is a village near Swords and Dublin Airport, and is set in a mainly rural area.

Swords is currently the third largest town in the Republic of Ireland. It is also home to the impressive Swords Castle.

Malahide is a coastal suburban town. Spreading from its town centre are extensive residential areas. It is home to Malahide Castle, which dates back to the twelfth century and today is a tourist attraction with many amenities.

Collinstown is home to Dublin Airport, Ireland's largest airport.

The Abbey Tavern

Abbey Street, Howth, Co Dublin
(1) 839 0307
info@abbeytavern.ie, www.abbeytavern.ie
Formerly part of the Old Abbey Monastery, this is now a traditional old-world local bar with open fires burning in winter. It is about three minutes' walk from Howth harbour, and is also home to The Loft restaurant. Food is served in the bar every day and there is regular entertainment.

_ _/_ _/20_ _

Bá Mizu

The Baily Hotel, Main Street, Howth, Co Dublin
Situated in The Baily Hotel, this bar was previously called The Coach House. It is currently closed.

_ _/_ _/20_ _

The Balrothery Inn

Dublin Road, Balrothery, Co Dublin
(1) 841 2252
Established around 1656 this traditional local pub was previously called The Merry Cricketer and is still sometimes referred to by this name. Scenes from the film *Murphy's Law* were filmed here. A separate entrance at the other side, with a notice 'Innkeeper 1656 J. McCormack & Sons' leads to a section of the pub called The Town of the Knights—this is the English translation of *Baile na Ródíre* or Balrothery. Food is served every day and there is regular entertainment.

_ _/_ _/20_ _

Bewley's Hotel Bar

Bewley's Hotel, Baskin Lane, Swords, Co Dublin, (1) 871 1000
dublinairport@bewleyshotels.com
www.bewleyshotels.com
A hotel bar and brasserie frequented by Dublin Airport travellers and also used as a business conference centre. Bewley's started out in the 1840s as a tea and coffee emporium.

_ _/_ _/20_ _

The Black Raven

3 Church Street, Skerries, Co Dublin
A traditional local pub established circa 1900. This house was called Jenbinis for a short time and reverted to the name The Black Raven in 2009. Prior to this it was called Christie Jenkson's. The clientele are very sport-focused.

_ _/_ _/20_ _

The Bloody Stream

Howth Railway Station, Howth, Co Dublin, (1) 839 5076
info@bloodystream.ie, www.bloodystream.ie
A bar and restaurant housed in the ground floor of Howth's Dart station, named after the stream flowing below the building which became bloodstained after a battle at the Evora Bridge in 1177. There is a Mediterranean-style beer garden, and regular entertainment.

_ _/_ _/20_ _

Blue Café Bar

Harbour Road, Skerries, Co Dublin
(1) 849 0900
info@bluebar.ie
www.bluebar.ie
A local café, bar and grill with great views over Skerries harbour. Food is served every day and there is occasional entertainment.

_ _/_ _/20_ _

The Boot Inn

Pickardstown, Cloghran, Co Dublin
(1) 844 4314
This is a traditional local pub, previously home to Jet's Nightclub. It is close to Dublin Airport. The pub was established in 1593, and is thus one of the oldest pubs in Ireland.

_ _/_ _/20_ _

The Brook Portrane

Portrane, Donabate, Co Dublin, (1) 843 6030
Moynihan's The Brook is a family-run local traditional pub, established in 1896 along the North Co Dublin coast. It was previously called Keeling's. The pub got its current name from a nearby river. There is a long beach behind the pub where you can go for fantastic walks (find the caves!) and then call into the pub for a pint and a chat. As a teenager I worked here for many summers along with my late father, Con Moloney. The pub has entertainment occasionally.

_ _/_ _/20_ _

The Carlyan

The Square, Lower Main Street, Rush, Co Dublin
(1) 843 8668
A traditional local pub, with occasional entertainment, previously called Armstrong's, Crean's, Flynn's and Kelly's. Its current name comes from Carlyan Rock, in Rush Harbour. This is a section of the carboniferous rocks that extend across North Co Dublin which can be seen at low tide on the coast at Rush.

_ _/_ _/20_ _

Carroll's Pierhouse

The Pierhouse Hotel, Harbour Road, Skerries, Co Dublin
A traditional bar named after a nearby lighthouse and situated in The Pierhouse Hotel which also housed Shenanigans Nightclub, previously called Shag's Nightclub. This establishment is currently closed.

_ _/_ _/20_ _

The Coachman's Inn

Airport Road, Cloghran, Co Dublin
(1) 840 1227
A traditional roadhouse pub situated near Dublin Airport. The pub was established in 1790. Food is served every day.

_ _/_ _/20_ _

The Cock Tavern

Church Street, Howth, Co Dublin
A traditional local pub, hidden away up the hill, near the harbour. There is a light snack menu every day and occasional entertainment.

_ _/_ _/20_ _

The Cock Tavern

31 Main Street, Swords, Co Dublin
(1) 840 5366
info@cocktavernswords.com
www.cocktavernswords.com
Smyth's Cock Tavern is a traditional local heritage pub established in 1896. It serves food every day and there is regular entertainment.

_ _/_ _/20_ _

Coolquay Lodge

The Ward, Co Dublin
(1) 835 1466
A traditional local pub and restaurant, established circa 1980. Food is served in the pub every day.

_ _/_ _/20_ _

de Brún

Bridge Street, Balbriggan, Co Dublin
(1) 841 2940
A traditional local pub and club with regular entertainment. Their slogan is 'Time Well Spent'. There are mirrors and furnishings in the main bar which were used as props in *The Godfather*.

_ _/_ _/20_ _

The Deer Park Hotel Bar

The Deer Park Hotel, Howth, Co Dublin, (1) 832 2624
sales@deerpark.iol.ie, www.deerpark-hotel.ie
This hotel is in the grounds of Howth Castle, and is also home to a golf club, as well as the Four Earl restaurant and a spa. Food is served every day. There are great views of Dublin by day and night from the complex. It was established in 1981.

_ _/_ _/20_ _

The Drop Inn

Upper Main Street, Rush, Co Dublin
(1) 843 7461
Oglesby's The Drop Inn is a traditional local pub, established in 1839. It was previously called Granny O'Keefe's and also at one time was called Kelly's. I am told that it was given to a Master Kelly by his parents as a wedding present.

_ _/_ _/20_ _

Duffy's Bar and Lounge

Main Street, Malahide, Co Dublin
(1) 845 0735
duffysie@gmail.com
www.duffys.ie
Established in 1760 this traditional local pub and sports bar has traded as Duffy's since 1970. It was refurbished in 2011. The pub serves food every day and there is regular entertainment.

_ _/_ _/20_ _

The Estuary

North Street, Swords, Co Dublin
(1) 840 7499
A traditional local pub previously called The Big Tree—the River Ward runs behind it. It serves food every day and there is regular entertainment.

_ _/_ _/20_ _

Fanning's The Central Lounge

Bridge Street, Balbriggan, Co Dublin
(1) 841 2150
A traditional local pub. There is a snooker room at the back.

_ _/_ _/20_ _

Forty Four Main Street

Forty Four Hotel, 44 Main Street, Swords, Co Dublin
(1) 840 1308
fortyfourmainstreet@gmail.com
www.thesmithgroup.ie
A traditional bar and hotel in Swords village, previously The Hawthorn Hotel. Food is served every day and there is regular entertainment.

_ _/_ _/20_ _

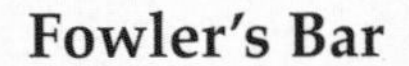

Fowler's Bar

12 New Street, Malahide, Co Dublin
(1) 845 0960
Known locally as Smyth's, as it was called by this name up to 2009 this traditional local pub was established in 1896. It was also previously called The Diamond Bar. Food is served every day and there is occasional entertainment.

_ _/_ _/20_ _

The Fox Inn

Ballymadun, Co Dublin
thefoxinn@live.ie
A traditional country pub with entertainment, usually on the last Friday of the month.

_ _/_ _/20_ _

The Garristown Inn

Main Street, Garristown, Co Dublin
This is a traditional country village pub, previously called Barbara Reid's. Food is served every day and there is regular entertainment. The pub is also home to The Windmill Restaurant

_ _/_ _/20_ _

Gibney's

New Street, Malahide, Co Dublin, (1) 845 0606
info@gibneys.com, www.gibneys.com
Trading as Gibney's since 1937 this traditional local pub has a strong sports following. The bar section is called The Caughoo Bar, after the winner of the 1947 Grand National. Some of the seats are directors' chairs from Arsenal Stadium.The pub has lots of history and memorabilia with famous signatures. A 20-foot deep well under the pub used to provide water to locals; it is now a wishing well. Food is served every day and there is regular entertainment.

_ _/_ _/20_ _

Gilbert & Wright The Living Room

1 Ross Lane, New Street, Malahide, Co Dublin
(1) 845 6580
malahide@gilbertandwright.ie
www.gilbertandwright.ie
A local pub set in a candlelit room with a 1970s theme. The pub has memorabilia, décor and sofas from this era and the 70s music in the background adds to the atmosphere. Food is served on weekday evenings and all day Saturday and Sunday. There is regular entertainment.

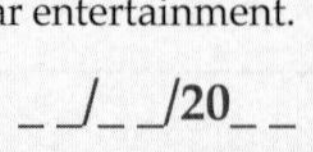
_ _/_ _/20_ _

Gilbert & Wright Wine Bar

Unit 14, The Plaza, Malahide Street,
Swords, Co Dublin, (1) 840 8400
swords@gilbertandwright.ie
www.gilbertandwright.ie
This is not just a wine bar, it is actually a full bar, 1970s-themed, with lots of bric à brac throughout, all set in a candle-lit room. It opened in 2007.

_ _/_ _/20_ _

The Gladstone Inn

The Cross, Skerries, Co Dublin
Hidden away just off the main street of Skerries, this traditional local pub was established in the early 1800s. It was previously called Boylan's. Mary Byrne, a finalist on the 2010 UK X Factor show, is a regular visitor with her family to Skerries and to the Gladstone Inn where she sang as a child. There is a framed newspaper cutting in the bar which highlights Mary's rise to fame, with the headline 'It all started in The Gladstone'.

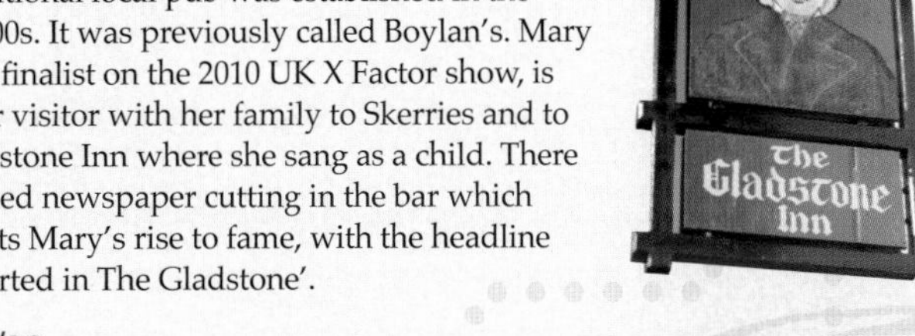

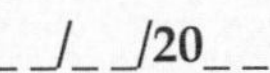
_ _/_ _/20_ _

The Golf Links

Strand Road, Portmarnock, Co Dublin
(1) 846 0129
O'Dwyer's Golf Links is a traditional local bar and lounge, established in 1961. It serves food every day and there is regular entertainment. The lounge offers a great view of the coast. Some locals call the pub The Widow's. There is a green area nearby which seems to attract large numbers of ducks, so bring along some bread!

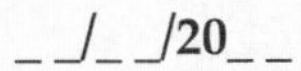
_ _/_ _/20_ _

Gormley's

Main Street, Garristown, Co Dublin
(1) 835 4261
This traditional local pub was established in 1887. It has entertainment occasionally.

_ _/_ _/20_ _

Hamlet

Castlemills Centre, Hamlet Lane, Balbriggan, Co Dublin
(1) 690 5394
hamletpub@eircom.net
Surrounded by new apartments and shops, this traditional local pub was established in 2007 just outside the town of Balbriggan. Food is served every day and there is regular entertainment.

_ _/_ _/20_ _

The Harbour Bar

Lower Main Street, Rush, Co Dublin
(1) 843 8937
Also known as Mooney's this pub on the Rush coast was named The Royal Oak when it was established circa 1700. It was known as a smugglers' pub. It has regular entertainment and houses a grill restaurant. It was a big music venue back in the day—Aslan, The Blades, The Lookalikes and Who's Eddie played here.

_ _/_ _/20_ _

The Harp Bar and Lounge

Carnegie Court Hotel, North Street, Swords, Co Dublin
(1) 840 4384
info@carnegiecourt.com, www.carnegiecourt.com
A lounge and club spread over two floors in the hotel which is also home to The Courtyard Restaurant and Jade Wine Bar. If you fancy clubbing later on, try the nightclub next door (now called Rouge, previously Velvet) which is open at weekends. Food is served every day in the lounge and there is regular entertainment.

_ _/_ _/20_ _

The Harvest Inn

Drogheda Street, Balbriggan, Co Dublin
(1) 841 1265
info@theharvest.ie
www.theharvest.ie
This traditional local pub was established in 1890 and rebuilt in 1923. There is food every day and regular entertainment. The pub is also home to Harvey's American Bar and Grill upstairs.

_ _/_ _/20_ _

Island View Bar

Island View Hotel, Coast Road, Malahide, Co Dublin, (1) 845 0099
info@islandviewhotel.ie, www.islandviewhotel.ie
A bar within The Island View Hotel which also houses Oscar Taylor's Restaurant. A section of the bar is known as Pete's Bar, named after one of the customers, now deceased, who was always found on the premises during opening hours. A portrait of Pete is hanging over the fireplace in the bar. The hotel was previously known as Stewart's Hotel. There is food every day and regular entertainment.

_ _/_ _/20_ _

Jack Doyle's Bar

The Bracken Court Hotel, Bridge Street, Balbriggan, Co Dublin
(1) 841 3333
info@brackencourt.ie, www.brackencourt.ie
Food is served every day in this traditional local hotel bar and there is regular entertainment. The hotel also houses The Bracken Grill.

_ _/_ _/20_ _

The Jameson Bar and The Cocktail Bar

Portmarnock Hotel, Strand Road, Portmarnock, Co Dublin, (1) 846 0611
info@portmarnock.com, www.portmarnock.com
These bars are in The Portmarnock Hotel, 'where nothing is overlooked but the sea'. The hotel was built on part of the former estate of the Jameson family of whiskey fame. The bar is housed in the original Jameson house, St Marnock's. It boasts panelled walls and ornate ceilings. Food is served every day and there is regular entertainment. The hotel is also home to The Cocktail Bar and The Osborne Brasserie.

_ _/_ _/20_ _

Joe May's

Harbour Road, Skerries, Co Dublin
(1) 849 1241
A traditional local coastal pub, established in the late 1800s, popular with bikers. A section of the bar has a low ceiling, about five foot six inches high. There is a sign on an internal door which reads 'All beer served on these premises has been passed by the landlord'. The pub serves a light snack menu and there is occasional entertainment.

_ _/_ _/20_ _

Kealy's of Cloghran

Old Airport Road, Cloghran / Corballis, Co Dublin
(1) 840 1372
mail@kealysofcloughran.ie, www.kealysofcloghran.ie
Close to Dublin Airport this traditional roadhouse dates back to 1901. Previously called Wood's and Murtagh's it has been trading as Kealy's since 1964. Food is served every day and there is regular entertainment.

_ _/_ _/20_ _

Keane's Bus Bar

Main Street, Skerries, Co Dublin
(1) 849 1282
A traditional local pub. It is called the Bus Bar after a bus terminus outside the pub.

_ _/_ _/20_ _

Keeling's

Main Street, Donabate, Co Dublin
(1) 843 6601
Known locally to older patrons as Joe's this traditional local pub, with a bar, lounge and snug, was established in 1892. There is regular entertainment.

_ _/_ _/20_ _

Kettle's The Inn

Kettle's Country House Hotel, Lispopple, Swords, Co Dublin
(1) 813 8511
info@kettleshotel.ie
www.kettleshotel.ie
A lounge, bar and snug situated in Kettle's Country House Hotel, just past Swords. It has been well extended over the years. It has a lounge at one end of the hotel and a bar at the other end, Sam's Snug sports bar, where you will find some of the locals. It was previously called The Rolestown Inn. Food is served every day and there is regular entertainment.

_ _/_ _/20_ _

Killian's

The Naul, Co Dublin
A traditional family-run village pub established around 1600, with open fires at each end of the house in winter. A light snack menu is served every day and there is regular entertainment.

_ _/_ _/20_ _

Kinsealy Inn

Feltrim Road, Kinsealy / Swords, Co Dublin
(1) 840 9449
A traditional local pub established in 1988. Food is served every day and there is regular entertainment. The pub also has a snooker room.

_ _/_ _/20_ _

Kittyhawks Bar and Bistro

The Carlton Hotel, Old Airport Road, Cloghran, Co Dublin, (1) 866 7500
info.dublin@carlton.ie, www.carltondublinairport.com
This is the bar of The Carlton Hotel, which is close to Dublin Airport. Food is served in the bar every day. Kittyhawk is the name of a town in North East Carolina, where the Wright brothers made their first flight. The hotel also houses Cloud's Rooftop Restaurant, which is mainly used for functions and weddings.

_ _/_ _/20_ _

Kruger's Top House

19 Main Street, Howth, Co Dublin
(1) 839 6636
krugers@eircom.net
A traditional local pub, situated halfway up the hill. There is food every day and regular entertainment.

_ _/_ _/20_ _

Kudos

The Clarion Hotel, Dublin Airport, Cloghran, Co Dublin
(1) 808 0500
kudos@clarionhoteldublinairport.com
www.clarionhoteldublinairport.com
The bar of The Clarion Hotel in the Dublin Airport complex. It has food every day and occasional entertainment. The hotel is also home to Kudos Restaurant and Savour Lounge.

_ _/_ _/20_ _

The Lord Mayor's

Main Street, Swords, Co Dublin, (1) 840 9455
A traditional pub, established in 1668 as The Royal Oak, famous for its thatched roof. The pub has the oldest surviving licence in Swords. It was once home to a handball alley. It was previously called O'Toole's, though the O'Toole family renamed it as The Bridge House. It was later owned by the Savage family, who gave it its current name. Food is served every day and there is regular entertainment.

_ _/_ _/20_ _

The Lounge

Balbriggan Harbour, Balbriggan, Co Dublin
(1) 841 3257
A traditional local pub and club situated at Balbriggan harbour, also home to two nightclubs, Home and Home After Dark. The bar and clubs are open at the weekend. The Lounge was previously called the Cardy Marina, Harbour Knights and O'Shea's.

_ _/_ _/20_ _

The Malting House Inn

The Holmpatrick, Skerries, Co Dublin
(1) 849 1077
maltinghouse@hotmail.com
A traditional local pub with accommodation first licensed in 1874. Its previous name was Kilmartin's. It is a well-known stop-off for bikers.

_ _/_ _/20_ _

The Man O' War

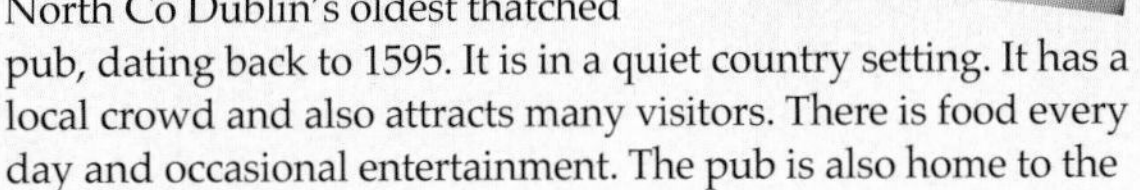

Courtlough, Balbriggan, Co Dublin
(1) 841 4052
info@manowar.ie, www.manowar.ie
North Co Dublin's oldest thatched pub, dating back to 1595. It is in a quiet country setting. It has a local crowd and also attracts many visitors. There is food every day and occasional entertainment. The pub is also home to the Seafood and Steakhouse Restaurant.

_ _/_ _/20_ _

Mangan's

42 Church Street, Skerries, Co Dublin
A traditional local pub, previously called The Fingal's Cave and The Michael Collins. This establishment is currently closed.

_ _/_ _/20_ _

The Manor Inn

Brackenstown Road, Swords, Co Dublin
(1) 895 6185
A traditional local pub, established around 1992. It was previously called Annie Oakley's Saloon Bar. It has regular entertainment.

_ _/_ _/20_ _

Matt Ryan's Bar

The Grand Hotel, Coast Road, Malahide, Co Dublin
(1) 845 0000
info@thegrand.ie
www.thegrand.ie
Hotel bar of The Grand Hotel Malahide, which is situated by the coast and is also home to The Coast restaurant. The hotel was established in 1835. Food is served every day in the Palm Court carvery.

_ _/_ _/20_ _

McCormack's

Balscadden, Co Dublin
(1) 802 0313
mccormackpub@gmail.com
www.mccormackspub.ie
Anthony McCormack's is a traditional country pub. It was established in 1871. Food is served every day and there is regular entertainment.

_ _/_ _/20_ _

The Michael Collins

Lower Main Street, Rush, Co Dublin
(1) 843 7249
A traditional local pub, previously called The Cradlerock. The pub is also home to The Latino Restaurant upstairs. There is regular entertainment in the bar.

_ _/_ _/20_ _

The Milestone

Drogheda Street, Balbriggan, Co Dublin
(1) 841 2176
theharvest@eircom.net
A pub has stood on this site for many years. The Milestone, which is a traditional pub, was built in 1923. There is food every day and regular entertainment.

_ _/_ _/20_ _

The Millrace

3 Dublin Street, Balbriggan, Co Dublin
(1) 883 4445
themillrace@gmail.com
Previously called John D's this traditional local pub is very much into sport. There is regular entertainment.

_ _/_ _/20_ _

Morgan's Kitchen and Bar

16 Main Street, Skerries, Co Dublin
(1) 849 5019
A traditional local pub, opened under this name in 2012. It was previously called The Dublin Bar, The Tavern, Tommy Bahamas, The Monument, Paparazzi Bar and Restaurant and most recently Jack's Bar and Grill. Food is served every day.

_ _/_ _/20_ _

Murray's

The Square, Lusk, Co Dublin
(1) 843 7237
A traditional local pub, offering a light snack menu every day and regular entertainment. The part of the pub now called Schroeder's Sports Bar was previously called The Stage Club.

_ _/_ _/20_ _

Murtagh's Roadhouse

Ballough, Balbriggan, Co Dublin
A traditional local pub, also known as Ballough House. It is currently closed.

_ _/_ _/20_ _

Nealon's

12 Church Street, Skerries, Co Dublin
(1) 849 0061
info@nealons.ie
www.nealons.ie
A traditional local pub with a great beer garden. 'You are a stranger here but once.' This pub was established circa 1890 and offers regular entertainment. It was previously called Gibney's and M. Tegan's.

_ _/_ _/20_ _

The Oasis Bar and Grill

The White Sands Hotel, Coast Road, Portmarnock, Co Dublin
(1) 866 6000
info@whitesandshotel.ie, www.whitesandshotel.ie
Hotel bar of The White Sands Hotel. Food is served every day and there is regular entertainment in the bar. The hotel is also home to Tamango Nightclub, known to its patrons over the years as 'Tamango's where the gang goes'. The club opens every Friday and Saturday, and on Wednesday during the summer. The hotel was established circa 1980.

_ _/_ _/20_ _

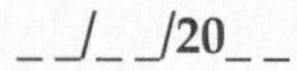

O'Connell's

4 East Pier, Howth, Co Dublin, (1) 839 5087
Located opposite Howth harbour, this traditional Irish pub was previously called The Pier House and was home to The Cibo Bar. When flying into Dublin Airport and sitting on the left side of the plane this is the first pub you can see. In the early 1900s it traded as Butson's Hotel Luncheon and Tea Rooms. It has traded as O'Connell's since 2012 and was first opened as a pub in 1971. Food is served every day and there is regular entertainment.

_ _/_ _/20_ _

O'Connor's Village Inn

Ballyboughal Village, Co Dublin
(1) 843 3102
This traditional village pub was closed for about four years before reopening in 2009. It was sorely missed, as it is the only pub in the village. It offers regular entertainment.

_ _/_ _/20_ _

O'Dea's

Radisson Blu Airport Hotel, Dublin Airport, Cloghran, Co Dublin, (1) 844 6000
info.airport.dublin@radissonblu.com
www.airport.dublin.radissonsas.com
A bar and grill situated in The Radisson Blu Airport Hotel, a a few minutes from Dublin Airport. The bar is named after the famous comedian, Jimmy O'Dea. Food is served every day.

_ _/_ _/20_ _

The Old Boro

Main Street, Swords, Co Dublin
(1) 895 7445
oldboroughpub@eircom.net
www.thesmithgroup.ie

This pub was an old schoolhouse from 1804 until 2000, when it was transformed into a large pub and club with an impressive finish. Its tall bar is constructed from fine timbers and is decorated with mirrors and large old clocks. It serves food every day and there is regular entertainment.

_ _/_ _/20_ _

The Old School House

Church Road, Coolbanagher, Swords, Co Dublin
(1) 840 4160

Opened as a bar and restaurant in 2005 this traditional local bar used to be an old schoolhouse. There is regular entertainment.

_ _/_ _/20_ _

The Oldtown House

Oldtown, Co Dublin
(1) 843 3247

A traditional local country village pub which can be traced back to the late 1700s. It was previously called White's.

_ _/_ _/20_ _

Ollie's Place

16–17 New Street, Skerries, Co Dublin
01 8494037
www.ollies.ie

A modern bar and grill serving food seven days a week in a contemporary New York style—'Ollie's Place . . . Your Place.' There is regular entertainment.

_ _/_ _/20_ _

Peacock Pub and Restaurant

River Valley Shopping Centre, Swords, Co Dublin
(1) 840 8969
Previously called The Millennium Bar, this traditional local pub and restaurant was established in 1988. Upstairs is home to The Steak House restaurant. There is regular entertainment.

_ _/_ _/20_ _

The Orchard

2 Applewood Village Green,
Swords, Co Dublin
(1) 840 9939
A traditional local pub, established in 2002. There is regular entertainment.

_ _/_ _/20_ _

The Pound Bar (McGrane's)

Bridge Street, Swords, Co Dublin
(1) 840 2223
McGrane's Pound Bar is just off the main street in Swords, this traditional local pub was previously called O'Connor's and Paschal McGrane's. It has regular entertainment.

_ _/_ _/20_ _

Premier Inn Bar and Bistro

The Premier Inn Hotel, Airside Retail Park, Swords, Co Dublin, (1) 895 7777
www.premierinn.com
The hotel was previously called The Tulip Hotel. Food is served in the bar every day.

_ _/_ _/20_ _

Raff's on the Corner

Church Street, Skerries, Co Dublin, (01) 8105650
info@raffsonthecorner.com,www.raffsonthecorner.com
Jimmy Rafferty, of the musical duo Rafferty & Halligan, is the proprietor of this modern local pub restaurant which opened in 2012. The duo regularly play at the pub. 'Live music, food and drink'. The establishment also bears the names The Parlour, Centre Stage and Coast Live Sports. It was previously called The Coast Inn and was home to Harvey's Restaurant.

_ _/_ _/20_ _

Simon Rutledge The White House

Newpark, The Ward, Co Dublin, (1) 834 2683
info@whitehouse.ie, www.whitehouse.ie
One of the great historic pubs and inns of Ireland, first established in 1620. The pub also has a guesthouse/motel and a pitch & putt course. It was previously called The Red Lion. Food is served every day and there is regular entertainment.

_ _/_ _/20_ _

Sapphire's Oriental Restaurant

Old Road, Rush, Co Dublin
(1) 870 9248
A local bar and restaurant. It was previously called Coyote Saloon and The Old Mill.

_ _/_ _/20_ _

The Schooner

27 Balbriggan Street, Skerries, Co Dublin
(1) 849 1261
A traditional local pub, established in 1930. Its name changed from The Schooner to Tony Daury's, then to Dunne's Lounge before returning to The Schooner in 2011. There is regular entertainment.

_ _/_ _/20_ _

Sherman's The Strand

Main Street, Rush, Co Dublin
(1) 843 7243
joeshermamstrand@gmail.com
A traditional local pub established circa 1600 as an inn. This pub was previously called Connolly's. Food is served every day and there is regular entertainment.

_ _/_ _/20_ _

The Slaughtered Lamb

EST. 1860

16 Main Street, Swords, Co Dublin
(1) 840 7263
info@theslaughteredlamb.com
www.theslaughteredlamb.com
One of Sword's largest venues, with five bars: The Cocktail Bar, The Code Bar, The Kokoro Lounge, The Pool Room and The Whiskey Bar. It also houses The Slaughtered Lamb Nightclub. Food is served every day and there is regular entertainment. The pub was established in 1860.

_ _/_ _/20_ _

Smyth's The Bridge House

Donabate, Co Dublin
(1) 843 5253
smythsbridge@eircom.net
T. J. Smyth The Bridge House is a traditional local pub, next to Donabate railway station. Paul, the proprietor, says that the pub is full of character and full of characters. It was established in the same year as the Guinness Brewery, one minute to six — 1759!

_ _/_ _/20_ _

The Snug

16–17 New Street, Skerries, Co Dublin
01 8494949
The Snug Bar has a 1960s theme, with many old items throughout, including valve radios and Bakelite telephones. Its previous names were Finnegan's, Halton's, Matthew's Bar, O'Shea's and The Windmill. The pub is connected to The Windmill Steakhouse Restaurant next door.

_ _/_ _/20_ _

Stoop Your Head

Harbour Road, Skerries, Co Dublin, (1) 849 2085
mayhilary@hotmail.com, www.stoopyourhead.ie
A family-run seafood restaurant and bar overlooking Skerries harbour, first established circa 1900. There is a low opening (approximately 5 foot 6 inches) in the wall dividing the bar into two rooms. This opening has padding on it and a sign which says STOOP YOUR HEAD. I am told that the pub was once called The Grosvenor House.

_ _/_ _/20_ _

Summit Inn

The Summit, Howth, Co Dublin
(1) 832 4615
The highest pub in Howth. Gaffney's traditional local pub was established circa 1850 and has traded as The Summit since 1950. Scenes from the films *The Snapper* and *Trojan Eddie* were shot here. Food is served every day and there is regular entertainment.

_ _/_ _/20_ _

M. R. Taylor The Star

Main Street, Swords, Co Dublin
(1) 840 5103
A traditional local pub and nightclub. The Zavedenie Club, connected to the pub, opens on Saturdays. Food is served every day and there is regular entertainment.

_ _/_ _/20_ _

TGI Friday's

Airside Retail Park, Swords, Co Dublin
(1) 840 8525
swords@fridays.ie
www.fridays.ie
Opened in 2012 this is a branch of the American restaurant and bar. The interior is filled with interesting items which include various kinds of automobile, musical and sports memorabilia.

_ _/_ _/20_ _

Top Shop

Main Street, Lusk, Co Dublin
A traditional local pub with regular entertainment. A poster of a Guinness label in the bar reads 'Guinness bottled by Jeremiah Murray'.

_ _/_ _/20_ _

Tower Bar and Bistro

Waterside House Hotel, Donabate, Co Dublin
(1) 843 6153
info@watersidehousehotel.ie
www.watersidehousehotel.ie
A bar and bistro housed in The Waterside House Hotel beside the sea next to the Donabate Martello tower. The bar, previously called The Clubhouse Bar, has a great beer garden. Food is served every day and there is regular entertainment. The hotel is also home to The Signal Restaurant.

_ _/_ _/20_ _

Walsh's

Main Street, Rush, Co Dublin
(1) 843 7394
An old-style traditional local pub, established in 1780. The bar is called Joe's Bar. At one time The Workshop Lounge was a saddlery.

_ _/_ _/20_ _

Waterside Lounge and Fisherman's Bar

Harbour Road, Howth, Co Dublin
(1) 839 0555
Situated near Howth harbour, this traditional local early house was previously called Cassidy's Waterside Lounge and The Evora Lounge. It was established around 1900. Food is served every day and there is regular entertainment. The pub is also home to El Paso Mexican Restaurant.

_ _/_ _/20_ _

The White Hart Inn

Dublin Street, Balbriggan, Co Dublin
(1) 841 2190
Known as 'Balbriggan's Premier Sports Bar' McCormack's Whitehart Inn is a traditional local pub with regular entertainment. It has many sporting pictures in the bar.

_ _/_ _/20_ _

Wright's Café Bar

Malahide Street, Swords, Co Dublin
(1) 840 6744
info@wrightscafebar.ie
www.wrightscafebar.ie
A large modern pub, spread over different levels. It was established in 2001 in the heart of Swords. Food is served every day and there is regular entertainment.

_ _/_ _/20_ _

Wright's Findlater

Harbour Road, Howth, Co Dublin
(1) 832 4488
Info@wrightsfindlaterhowth.com
www.findlater.ie
This modern café bar and grill which opened in 2005 is one of Howth's newest landmarks. The Sky Bar at the top of the building offers great views northwards along the east coast. There is regular entertainment. The St Laurence Hotel which dates back to 1840 previously traded on this site, and also housed Saints Nightclub.

_ _/_ _/20_ _

The Yacht Bar

Loughshinny, Skerries, Co Dublin
This traditional local pub, also known as Murthy Mahon's, is currently closed.

_ _/_ _/20_ _

South County Dublin

Glencullen, Leopardstown, Booterstown, Stillorgan, Kilmacud, Goatstown, Mount Merrion, Blackrock, Monkstown, Dún Laoghaire, Deansgrange, Kill of the Grange, Glasthule, Sandycove, Dalkey, Killiney, Loughlinstown, Ballybrack and Shankill

The DART suburban railway network runs along much of the Dublin coast, from Howth to Greystones.

Glencullen is a village and a townland in the civil parish of Kilternan. At the centre of the village is Johnnie Fox's Pub, which was established in 1798, the year of the Irish Rebellion led by Wolfe Tone. Glencullen is also near to the impressive Three Rock mountain.

Leopardstown, meaning 'Town of the Lepers', is located at the foot of the Dublin mountains. It is a residential suburb, bordering Sandyford, Stepaside, Ballyogan, Foxrock and Stillorgan. The area is home to the famous Leopardstown Racecourse.

Booterstown is home to the Booterstown Bird Sanctuary, situated alongside the DART suburban rail line.

Stillorgan, formerly a village, has now developed into a large residential area. The original Celtic name for Stillorgan was Athnakill—'Place of the Church'. Stillorgan's shopping centre, which opened in 1965, was Ireland's first purpose-built shopping centre.

Kilmacud is a suburban area west of Stillorgan village, east of Dundrum and south of Goatstown. Most of its housing development took place in the 1950s.

Mount Merrion is a middle-class suburb situated next to Blackrock and Stillorgan. The area was originally estate lands which over time were sold off and developed into a residential area. Mount Merrion is also home to Deer Park, a public park which also contains sporting facilities.

Blackrock is a suburban town just north of Dún Laoghaire. In the nineteenth century the area began to be developed. It is home to a park that stretches from Blackrock to Booterstown. Many fine houses were built in the area, the most famous of which was Frescati House, the childhood home of Lord Edward FitzGerald.

Monkstown is a village and residential area located on the coast between Blackrock and Dún Laoghaire. One of Monkstown's main features is Monkstown Castle, built around the twelfth century. Notable people who have resided in the area include U2's The Edge, Sinead O'Conner and Chris de Burgh.

Dún Laoghaire is the principal town in South County Dublin. It is also the second port of Dublin. It has a large pier, The Pavilion theatre, a cinema, and two shopping centres. It is also home to St Michael's Hospital, which first opened its doors to patients in 1876.

Deansgrange is a suburban area near Dún Laoghaire, situated around a crossroads. The area further east of Deansgrange is known as Kill of the Grange, translated as Grange Church. The original church is now in ruins.

Glasthule is a suburban village located between Dún Laoghaire and Sandycove. It has many retail outlets and speciality shops.

Sandycove is most famous for its James Joyce Tower, where Joyce wrote part of *Ulysses*.

Dalkey is Dublin's only heritage town, boasting many visitor attractions, including some of the best views of Dublin and the Wicklow mountains.

Killiney is one of Dublin's most exclusive residential areas. Some of its famous residents include Bono, The Edge and Enya. Several foreign ambassadors also have their homes here. The area also has Killiney Hill Park, which boasts wonderful views of Dublin Bay, Killiney Bay, Bray Head and the Sugar Loaf mountain.

Loughlinstown is a residential suburb. It was originally a village on the road from Dublin to Bray, Co Wicklow. During the 1960s a dual carriageway was built through the area, causing the village to be shifted to the western side of the new road. Loughlinstown is also the location of St Colmcille's Hospital which serves both south Dublin and North Wicklow.

Ballybrack is a suburb located south of Killiney, and northeast of Loughlinstown. Sean Lemass, past Taoiseach, was born and lived in Ballybrack.

Shankill, meaning 'old church', is a residential suburb in the south-east of Dublin. Shankill has developed over time from small agricultural smallholdings into an area comprising of many housing estates. Notable residents include Padraig Harrington, golfing superstar, RTÉ sports commentator Des Cahill, and Eamon Gilmore, leader of the Irish Labour party.

40 Foot Bar and Grill

The Pavilion, Marine Road, Dún Laoghaire, Co Dublin
(1) 236 0663
info@fortyfoot.ie info@prive.ie, www.fortyfoot.ie
www.prive.ie
Named after the famous 40 Foot bathing area in nearby Sandycove, this is a modern bar next to the Pavilion Theatre in Dún Laoghaire, with Club Privé above the pub. It was known for a short time as Bodega but reverted to the 40 Foot name when it reopened under new management in 2009. The bar is on the upper level and has panoramic views of Dún Laoghaire harbour. Food is served every day.

_ _/_ _/20_ _

Avoca Bar and Restaurant

33 Carysfort Avenue, Blackrock, Co Dublin
(1) 288 0789
the.avoca@gmail.com
www.avocabar.com
A traditional local sports bar and lounge, serving food every day, and offering over 60 different craft beers. The pub was previously called The Ass and Cart. It was one of the first bars in Dublin to provide WiFi.

_ _/_ _/20_ _

Baker's Corner

1 Kill Avenue, Kill O' The Grange, Co Dublin
(1) 280 7782
www.johnbradygroup.ie
A traditional local pub. Food is served every day and there is regular entertainment.

_ _/_ _/20_ _

Boland's on the Hill

The Hill, Stillorgan, Co Dublin, (1) 2109760
Stillorgan's oldest pub, previously called Boland's Hill, The Stillorgan House and most recently McGowans of Stillorgan. In earlier times, it was a watering hole for South Dublin writers, including Myles na gCopaleen and the author of *The Quiet Man*, Maurice Walsh. John Wayne came in for drinks during the making of *The Quiet Man* in the 1950s. Food is served every day and there is regular entertainment.

_ _/_ _/20_ _

Conway's

Main Street, Blackrock, Co Dublin, (1) 278 4934
conwaysblackrock@hotmail.com
Sections of the bar in this traditional local pub were reclaimed from an old schoolhouse. Food is served every day and there is regular entertainment.

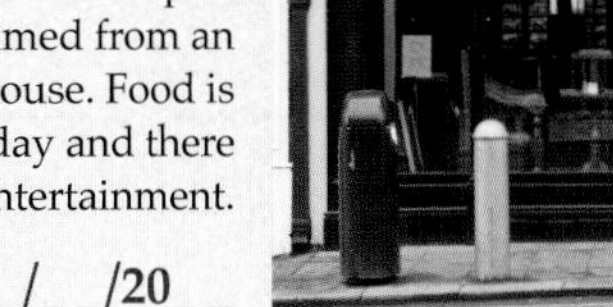

_ _/_ _/20_ _

The Breffni

10 Main Street, Blackrock, Co Dublin, (1) 288 8759
A traditional local pub serving food every day.

_ _/_ _/20_ _

The Club

107 Coliemore Road, Dalkey, Co Dublin, (1) 285 8511
www.theclubdalkey.com
A traditional local bar and restaurant, established in 1840 and called The Queenstown Tavern until 1944. It has been run by the Sheeran family since 1969. It was a favourite haunt of playwright Hugh Leonard. Food is served every day.

_ _/_ _/20_ _

Brady's of Shankill

Shankill Town Centre, Shankill, Co Dublin, (1) 282 0153
robbie@johnbradygroup.ie, www.johnbradygroup.ie
Previously known as The Shankill Hotel this traditional local pub was established in the early 1800s. It is home to Mickey Byrne's bar. Food is served every day and there is regular entertainment.

_ _/_ _/20_ _

Byrne's Galloping Green

Galloping Green, Stillorgan Road, Stillorgan, Co Dublin, (1) 288 7683
Also known as Philipstown House and previously known as Gerry Byrne's, this traditional local pub's current name derives from a miniature racecourse in this location many years ago. The pub was established in 1879. A light snack menu is served every day.

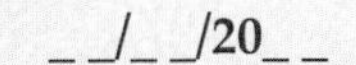

_ _/_ _/20_ _

The Druid's Chair

Killiney Hill Road, Killiney, Co Dublin, (1) 285 7297
thedruidschair@gmail.com
This traditional local pub is named after an ancient stone formation which can be seen nearby. The pub is housed in a building that dates back to 1882. Food is served every day and there is regular entertainment.

_ _/_ _/20_ _

COIRNÉAL UÍ DHONNCHAIDH
DUNPHY'S CORNER

Dunphy's

41 Lower George's Street, Dún Laoghaire, Co Dublin, (1) 280 1668
A traditional local pub, established in 1930, serving a light snack menu every day. A street sign fitted in 2011 on the side of the pub bears the name 'Dunphy's Corner'. This is in reference to Thomas Dunphy's pub (now Doyle's) in Phibsborough, mentioned in James Joyce's *Ulysses*.

_ _/_ _/20_ _

Eagles House

18–19 Glasthule Road, Glasthule, Co Dublin
(1) 280 4740
info@eagleshouse.ie
www.eagleshouse.ie
This traditional local pub was established in the early 1900s. Bono has been known to call in here for a drink. Food is served every day and there is regular entertainment.

_ _/_ _/20_ _

The Farmhouse Inn

Monkstown Farm, Dún Laoghaire, Co Dublin
(1) 280 2574
A traditional local pub with regular entertainment.

_ _/_ _/20_ _

Farrell's

Marine Road, Dún Laoghaire, Co Dublin
There are two entrances to this traditional local pub which is on the third floor of the Dún Laoghaire Shopping Centre: one via Marine Road which has a lift to the pub, and the other through the shopping centre. The pub, which was previously called The Leslie Inn, was established in 1974 and is full of characters. It has a large display of miniature spirit bottles and marine pictures. A light snack menu is served every day and there is regular entertainment.

_ _/_ _/20_ _

Finnegan's

2 Sorrento Road, Dalkey, Co Dublin, (1) 285 8505
www.finnegans.ie
A traditional local pub established around 1900. Previously called O'Mara's and Joe Larkin's it has traded as Finnegan's since 1970. It has a large selection of whiskeys 'to suit every palate'. Lunch is served every day. The lounge is called Sorrento Lounge.

_ _/_ _/20_ _

Fitzgerald's Albert House

11 Sandycove Road, Sandycove, Co Dublin, (1) 280 4469
fitzgeraldsofsandycove@yahoo.ie
www.fitzgeraldsofsandycove.com
Known locally as Fitzer's this traditional family-run pub was established in 1861 and has been trading as Fitzgerald's since 1960. It is near the James Joyce Museum in the Sandycove Martello Tower, and has many Joycean-themed pictures and stained glass windows. Food is served every day.

_ _/_ _/20_ _

Fitzpatrick Castle Hotel

Fitzpatrick Castle Hotel, Killiney, Co Dublin
(1) 230 5400
www.fitzpatrickhotels.com
This hotel, which opened in 1971, houses The Library Bar and The Dungeon Bar and Grill, as well as PJ's Restaurant. The castle was built in 1741. There is regular entertainment.

_ _/_ _/20_ _

Gilbert & Wright

128 Lower George's Street, Dún Laoghaire, Co Dublin
(1) 663 6148
dunlaoghaire@gilbertandwright.ie
www.gilbertandwright.ie
Opened in 2010 this pub has a 1970s theme with memorabilia, décor and sofas from this era throughout the bar, lighted candles in the fireplaces and 70s music in the background adding to the atmosphere. Food is served every day and there is regular entertainment. The pub was originally established in 1855, and was called J. Smyth and Son. It was rebuilt in 1925.

_ _/_ _/20_ _

Gleeson's of Booterstown

44 Booterstown Avenue, Booterstown, Co Dublin
(1) 288 0361
info@gleesons.ie, www.gleesons.ie
Previously called Sarah Murphy's Pub and Grocer this traditional local pub has traded as Gleeson's since 1954. Food is served every day. The pub was refurbished in 2010, with the addition of a delicatessan and off-licence called Food Corner. Willows Restaurant is upstairs.

_ _/_ _/20_ _

Goggins

99–101 Monkstown Road, Monkstown, Co Dublin
(1) 280 2735
A traditional local pub and sports bar. The Valparaiso Restaurant is upstairs. The pub was established in 1901. There is food every day and regular entertainment.

_ _/_ _/20_ _

The Graduate

Rochestown Avenue, Killiney, Co Dublin
(1) 285 2761
info@thegraduate.ie, www.thegraduate.ie
Burned to the ground in June 2009 this traditional local pub reopened in March 2010, looking almost the same as before. Over 120 miniature spirit bottles are on display in the bar, some of which were rescued from the fire. Food is served every day and there is regular entertainment.

_ _/_ _/20_ _

The Grange Pub

1 Deansgrange Road, Deansgrange, Co Dublin
(1) 289 5651
A traditional local pub with a bar and lounge, previously called Silk's Bar and Grocer, and later Foley's. The bar area is called Midway Bar as the pub is halfway between Dublin and Bray, Co Wicklow. Food is served every day and there is regular entertainment.

_ _/_ _/20_ _

Harbor Bar & Grill

6–7 Marine Road, Dún Laoghaire, Co Dublin, (1) 214 5772
info@harborbarandgrill.com, www.harborbarandgrill.com
A modern bar and restaurant with a covered front garden and regular entertainment. It is near Dún Laoghaire harbour and Dart station and is 'a pub with rooms', providing accommodation. It was previously called The Gastro Pub Company, and prior to that it was The Elphin Hotel.

_ _/_ _/20_ _

Hardy's Bar

The Royal Marine Hotel, Marine Road, Dún Laoghaire, Co Dublin, (1) 230 0030
info@royalmarine.ie, www.royalmarine.ie
A bar in The Royal Marine Hotel named after one of its famous guests, Oliver Hardy, of the great comedic duo, Laurel and Hardy, who stayed in the hotel for a month in 1953. It serves food every day and has a relaxed, friendly atmosphere. There is regular entertainment. A section of the bar is called Laurel's Bar. The hotel, which dates back to 1828, is also home to The Bay Lounge, The Dun Bistro Steak & Seafood Restaurant, and The Pavilion Bar, which is mostly used for functions.

_ _/_ _/20_ _

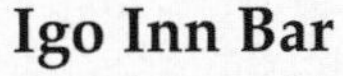

Igo Inn Bar

Military Road, Ballybrack, Co Dublin
(1) 282 4615
tom@johnbradygroup.ie
www.johnbradygroup.ie
A traditional local pub, previously called The Village Inn. It is home to The Cedar Lounge. Food is served every day and there is regular entertainment.

_ _/_ _/20_ _

Jack O'Rourke's

15 Main Street Blackrock, Co Dublin
(1) 288 7102
tgorourke@hotmail.com
www.jackororourkes.com
Established in the early 1800s as a bar and grocer this traditional local pub has traded as O'Rourke's since 1921. It was at one time called Laurence Wickham's. A letter from Myles na gCopaleen to Jack O'Rourke is displayed. Food is served every day and there is occasional entertainment.

_ _/_ _/20_ _

Johnnie Fox's

Glencullen, Co Dublin, (1) 295 5647
info@jfp.ie, www.jfp.ie
An old world pub established in 1798, this 'quintessential Irish pub' is famous for its traditional interior, full of artefacts and with sawdust on the flagstone floor. It is reputed to be Ireland's highest pub (1100 feet above sea level). Food is served every day and a long-running traditional show is put on every night. Many movie scenes and advertisements have been filmed here, including Guinness ads and episodes from *Lovejoy*. There is an express bus to and from the city centre every night.

_ _/_ _/20_ _

Kiely's of Mount Merrion

68 Deerpark Road, Mount Merrion, Co Dublin, (1) 283 2666
info@kielys.com, www.kielys.com
A traditional local pub, also known as The Sportsman's Inn. Established circa 1980 it was previously called The Stella House. Food is served every day and there is regular entertainment.

_ _/_ _/20_ _

The King's Inn

45 Castle Street, Dalkey, Co Dublin
(1) 285 8250
A traditional local pub, opposite The Queen's. It was established circa 1890 and was previously called Hogan's. There is entertainment on bank holiday weekends.

_ _/_ _/20_ _

The Leopardstown Inn

Brewery Road, Stillorgan, Co Dublin, (1) 288 9189
www.leopardstowninn.ie
A well-extended traditional local pub, serving food every day and offering regular entertainment. Within the pub are The Central Lounge, The Blue Bar, Reddy's Bar and The Carousel Cocktail Bar, the latter being Dublin's first revolving bar. The pub is also home to Green's Restaurant.

_ _/_ _/20_ _

Kozie II

73 Upper George's Street Upper, Dún Laoghaire, Co Dublin
(1) 284 1998
A traditional local pub, housed in a building that dates back to 1904. Food is served every day and there is regular entertainment.

_ _/_ _/20_ _

The Lough Inn

Unit 11, Loughlinstown Shopping Centre, Loughlinstown, Co Dublin
(1) 282 0809
Murphy's Lough Inn is a traditional local pub established in 1989. A snack menu is served and there is regular entertainment.

_ _/_ _/20_ _

Lime Bar

Upper George's Street, Dún Laoghaire, Co Dublin
This traditional local bar, previously called Nemo's, is currently closed.

_ _/_ _/20_ _

The Magpie Inn

115 Coliemore Road, Dalkey, Co Dublin
(1) 202 3909
info@magpieinn.com
www.magpieinn.com

Previously called The Arches and In Dalkey, this traditional local pub has traded as The Magpie since 2011. It was established around 1847. There are signs inside that read 'Eat, Drink and be Merry' and 'Two for Joy'. Food includes a large selection of seafood, and there is also a wide range of craft beers.

_ _/_ _/20_ _

P. McCormack & Sons

67 Lower Mounttown, Dún Laoghaire, Co Dublin
(1) 280 5519

A well-extended traditional local pub with a heated smoking area in a mature garden. Food is served every day. The pub, which has traded as McCormack's since the early 1960s, is often referred to by its previous name, Hand's. In the early 1990s, Jerry Lee Lewis's wife organised a party for him here. Apparently he brought the house down.

_ _/_ _/20_ _

McDonagh's

Castle Street, Dalkey, Co Dublin
(1) 285 0889

A traditional local pub and music venue, established in 1888 as McDonagh's and known locally as Mac's. For a time it was called Patrick Ivory's and The Raw Bar, reverting to its current name in 2010. Food is served every day and there is regular entertainment.

_ _/_ _/20_ _

Frank McKenna The Yacht Tavern

8 Wellington Street, Dún Laoghaire, Co Dublin
(1) 280 3970
Locally known as Dad's or Arthur's Place this traditional local family-run pub off Lower George's Street was established circa 1900. A light snack is served on weekdays and there is regular entertainment.

_ _/_ _/20_ _

The Melt 'n' Pot

20–22 Temple Road, Blackrock, Co Dublin
(1) 288 8337
meltnpot@gmail.com
This large modern pub was previously called Sheehan's and The Time Piece. Food is served every day.

_ _/_ _/20_ _

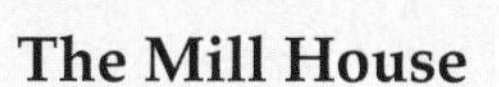

The Mill House

1 Lower Kilmacud Road, Stillorgan, Co Dublin
(1) 288 6206
A traditional local pub, serving food every day. It was established in 1963. One of the bars is known as Dicey Reilly's Bar.

_ _/_ _/20_ _

O'Donohoe's

17 Main Street, Blackrock, Co Dublin
Locally known as O'D's Pub this is a traditional local bar, with regular entertainment.

_ _/_ _/20_ _

O'Dwyer's

118 Lower Kilmacud Road, Stillorgan, Co Dublin
(1) 288 2228
odwyerkilmacud@eircom.net
A traditional local family-run pub, serving food every day. Upstairs you will find O'Dwyer's Café Bar. This pub was established in 1958.

_ _/_ _/20_ _

The Old Punch Bowl

116 Rock Road, Booterstown, Co Dublin
(1) 283 2356
Named after a three-gallon punchbowl this traditional local pub, bar and restaurant was established in 1719. The punchbowl was originally owned by the Duke of Leinster, and was often used to make punch for local funerals and gatherings. No one knows its whereabouts now. The pub serves food every day and there is regular entertainment.

_ _/_ _/20_ _

Oliveto Osteria Bar and Tea Rooms

The Kingston Hotel, Adelaide Street / 9–12 Haddington Terrace, Dún Laoghaire, Co Dublin, (1) 280 0011
reserv@kingstonhotel.com reservations@oliveto.ie
www.kingstonhotel.com www.oliveto.ie
A bar and tea room in The Kingston Hotel, a listed building which dates back to the late 19th century, when Dún Laoghaire was known as Kingstown. The hotel overlooks Dublin Bay and the East Pier and also has a beer garden facing the sea. The bar has regular entertainment. Up until 2011 the hotel bar was called The Carlisle Bar, no doubt after Carlisle Pier in Dún Laoghaire harbour.

_ _/_ _/20_ _

T. O'Loughlin

26 Lower George's Street, Dún Laoghaire, Co Dublin
(1) 280 7391
Known locally as Loughie's this traditional local pub has not changed much over the years. They use an old-style cash register which I am told was bought secondhand for £4 when the original Mr O'Loughlin first opened the pub in 1929. His sons, who are great personalities, regularly work here and there is always good craic and lots of banter.

_ _/_ _/20_ _

The Orangery Bar

St Helen's Radisson Blu Hotel, Stillorgan Road, Blackrock, Co Dublin, (1) 218 6000
info.dublin@radissonblu.com, www.radissonblu.ie
As its name suggests, this hotel bar is set in a Victorian conservatory. Food is served every day. The hotel is located in one of Dublin's historic estates, St Helen's Estate. It also houses Talavera Italian Restaurant and La Panto Restaurant.

_ _/_ _/20_ _

Palmer's Golden Ball

Kilternan Road, Kilternan, Co Dublin
(1) 295 5643
A traditional local pub at the foot of the Dublin Mountains, established in 1862. It has a snooker and pool room and there is food every day as well as regular entertainment.

_ _/_ _/20_ _

The Pub

3 The Crescent, Monkstown, Co Dublin
(1) 284 6187
fxbmonkstown@hotmail.com
www.fxbrestaurants.com
A gastro pub, home to FXB Restaurant. It has a picture gallery and paintings for sale by local artists is displayed in the pub. Food is served every day in the bar.

_ _/_ _/20_ _

The Purty Kitchen

Old Dun Leary Road, Dún Laoghaire, Co Dublin
(1) 284 3576
info@purtykitchen.con
www.purtykitchen.com
Established in 1728, and previously called The Dunleary Inn, this is a traditional local pub, club and a restaurant renowned for its chowder. There is regular entertainment in the bar. The pub is also home to The Loft music venue which is currently closed.

_ _/_ _/20_ _

The Queen's

12 Castle Street, Dalkey, Co Dublin
(1) 285 4569
www.thequeens.ie
A favourite lunch place for the writer Maeve Binchy who lived nearby, this traditional local bar and restaurant is home to The Vico Suite function room and offers regular entertainment. The pub was first licensed in 1787.

_ _/_ _/20_ _

The Rambler's Rest

Church Road, Ballybrack, Co Dublin
(1) 282 6338
This traditional local pub was established in 1878 as a coachhouse and inn. There is regular entertainment.

_ _/_ _/20_ _

Robbins

75 York Road, Dún Laoghaire, Co Dublin
A traditional local pub, previously called The Anchor Inn and Eugene Murphy's. It traded as Robbins from 2006 but is currently closed.

_ _/_ _/20_ _

The Rochestown Lodge Café Bar

The Rochestown Lodge Hotel, Rochestown Avenue, Dún Laoghaire, Co Dublin
(1) 285 3555
info@rochestownlodge.com
www.rochestown-lodge-hotel.com
The bar of in the Rochestown Lodge Hotel, previously called The Victor Hotel, which also houses a leisure centre and spa. Food is served every day in the bar and there is regular entertainment.

_ _/_ _/20_ _

The Sally Noggin Inn

Sallynoggin Road, Sallynoggin, Co Dublin
(1) 285 4602
info@thesallynogginInn.ie
www.thesallynogginInn.ie

Known locally as 'the Noggin' this local pub was established in 1951 and is famous for sports. It was a well-known cabaret venue some years ago and still has entertainment at weekends. 'Not just another pub.' Food is served every day.

_ _/_ _/20_ _

The Stillorgan Orchard

1 The Hill, Stillorgan, Co Dublin
(1) 288 6793
info@stillorganorchard.com
www.stillorganorchard.com

A modern café bar and music venue set in a house with 'the largest thatched roof in Ireland'. This pub was previously called Cullen's. Food is served every day.

_ _/_ _/20_ _

Scott's Café Bar

17 Upper George's Street,
Dún Laoghaire, Co Dublin
(1) 280 2657

Recently called The Lion Bar and Grill, and previously called Burke's and Mooney's, this traditional local pub reverted to the name Scott's in 2011. It was established circa 1930. Food is served every day and there is regular entertainment.

_ _/_ _/20_ _

The Silver Tassie

Bray Road, Loughlinstown, Co Dublin
(1) 282 2958
www.madigan.ie

Madigan's Silver Tassie is a traditional local roadhouse pub. Food is served every day and there is regular entertainment.

_ _/_ _/20_ _

TGI Friday's

Newtownpark Ave, Blackrock, Co Dublin
A branch of the American restaurant and bar chain, previously The Playhouse Inn. This establishment is currently closed.

_ _/_ _/20_ _

Weir's

88 Lower George's Street, Dún Laoghaire, Co Dublin, (1) 230 4654
A traditional local pub, housed in a building that dates back to 1898. Food is served every day.

_ _/_ _/20_ _

Tonic Bar Café Club

5 Temple Road, Blackrock, Co Dublin, (1) 288 7671
mail@tonic.ie, www.tonic.ie
A modern bar and home to the Suite 54 Club. It was previously called The Missing Swan. Food is served every day and there is regular entertainment.

_ _/_ _/20_ _

Walter's Café Bar

68 Upper George's Street,
Dún Laoghaire, Co Dublin
(1) 280 7442
A traditional local pub, also home to The Bay Restaurant on the upper level. Food is served every day and there is regular entertainment in the bar.

_ _/_ _/20_ _

The Wicked Wolf

2 Main Street, Blackrock,
Co Dublin, (1) 283 6424
A traditional local pub and venue with regular entertainment, established around 1940. It was previously called Byrne's, Collins' and Fitzers.

_ _/_ _/20_ _

The Wild Boar Pub

Unit 8 Stepaside Village, Stepaside, Co Dublin
(1) 205 2025
www.theboxtree.ie
Previously called Loughlin's Bar and Bistro, this pub was built in 2008 on the site where The Mountain View House Pub once stood. It opened as The Wild Boar Pub in 2010, and is now also home to The Box Tree Restaurant. Food is served every day.

_ _/_ _/20_ _

The Wishing Well

Newtown Park, Blackrock, Co Dublin
(1) 283 3970
A traditional local pub previously called The Dandy Inn and Maguire's. It has traded as The Wishing Well since around 1950. Food is served every day and there is regular entertainment.

_ _/_ _/20_ _

This board game, where players throw rings on to the hooks, is still played in a few Dublin pubs, including The Gravediggers in Glasnevin, The Man O'War and The Hideout House.

West County Dublin

Brittas, Hazelhatch, Lucan, Finnstown, Newcastle, Rathcoole and Saggart

Brittas is a village situated on the south west of Dublin, almost on the border of Wicklow.

Hazelhatch is an area on the border between County Kildare and County Dublin. The Grand Canal passes through the area, and fishing and boating takes place here.

Lucan is a suburban town located to the west of south Dublin. When a sulphurous spa was discovered in Lucan in the 1700s, it brought the townland into prominence. In recent years the area has undergone huge change regarding residential developments.

Finnstown is a locality situated within Lucan.

Newcastle is a village about 20 km west of Dublin, in a mainly rural area. In recent years there has been a sharp rise in population here.

Rathcoole is a suburban village, south west of Tallaght, and bordering the nearby village of Saggart. The name Rathcoole may have come from the combination of the Irish words *rath* and *coil*, respectively translated as 'ringfort' and 'forest'. Over the years much housing development has taken place in the area.

Saggart, translated as 'priest's house', is a suburban village west of Dublin. Saggart has some well-known objects of historical interest, including megalithic standing stones and a Celtic cross dating back to the tenth century.

An Poitín Stil

Naas Road, Rathcoole, Co Dublin, (1) 458 9244
anpoitinstill@fitzgeraldgroup.ie, www.louisfitzgerald.com
One of the few Dublin pubs with a thatched roof, this traditional local museum and roadhouse pub is well-known as a steakhouse and carvery. Established in 1694 it is the original stop-off for those travelling southbound from Dublin. There is a traditional copper still just inside the main door.

_ _/_ _/20_ _

The Ball Alley House

Lucan Road, Lucan, Co Dublin
(1) 628 0220
Previously a handball alley (hence the name) this is a traditional local pub. It hosts occasional entertainment.

_ _/_ _/20_ _

The Ballyneety Bar

The Spa Hotel, Junction 4A, N4 Westbound, Lucan, Co Dublin, (1) 628 0494
info@lucanspahotel.ie
www.lucanspahotel.ie
Hotel bar of The Spa Hotel, which dates back to 1758. Food is served every day and there is occasional entertainment.

_ _/_ _/20_ _

The Baurnafea House

Main Street, Rathcoole, Co Dublin
(1) 458 0842
A traditional local pub established circa 1980. It serves food every day.

_ _/_ _/20_ _

The Blackchurch Inn

Naas Road, Rathcoole, Co Dublin, (1) 458 9116
Once called Vicker's this traditional local pub is on the N7 motorway. It was formerly owned by the Irish comedian Brendan Grace. Food is served every day.

_ _/_ _/20_ _

The Blue Gardenia

Brittas, Co Dublin
Situated on the edge of Dublin past Tallaght, this traditional local pub was established in 1847 but is currently closed. It was a famous local landmark when it was known as Hotel Brittas. At one time it was owned by the traditional Irish band The Wolfe Tones. The outside of the building is painted in the Dublin football team colours.

_ _/_ _/20_ _

Courtney's

Main St, Lucan, Co Dublin, (1) 628 0251
info@courtneyslounge.com
www.courtneyslounge.com
Known locally as Bob's, this is a traditional local pub, famed for its thatched roof and beer garden themed around the Irish film *The Quiet Man*, with the White O'Morn Cottage within. Food is served every day and there is regular entertainment. The pub, which was established in 1830, was previously called R. Carroll's. It is also home to Duke's Bistro.

_ _/_ _/20_ _

The Foxhunter

Ballydowd Lucan West, Lucan, Co Dublin
(1) 626 2599
katiesfood@gmail.com
A traditional local pub that hosts events in The Taylor Quigley Function Room. It was previously known as Ma Langan's. Food is served every day and there is occasional entertainment.

_ _/_ _/20_ _

The Gondola

Main Street, Newcastle, Co Dublin
(1) 458 9231
This traditional local pub, previously called Dowling's Gondola, is a great place to watch sport. The bar is called St Finian's Bar and a wooden plaque behind the counter reads 'Golf spoken here'. There is horseracing memorabilia throughout the house. Food is served on Sundays and there is regular entertainment.

_ _/_ _/20_ _

The Hatch Bar

Hazelhatch Bridge, Hazelhatch/Newcastle, Co Dublin
A traditional local canal-side bar situated on Hazelhatch Bridge. The bridge dates back to 1791. The bar is currently closed.

_ _/_ _/20_ _

Jacob's

Main Street, Saggart, Co Dublin
(1) 458 9186
info@jacobsbar.ie
www.jacobsbar.ie
A traditional local pub, also home to The China Garden restaurant on the first floor. The pub was established in 1901. A light snack menu is served every day and there is regular entertainment.

_ _/_ _/20_ _

Jack Kavanagh's

Main Street, Saggart, Co Dublin
A traditional local pub. This pub is currently closed due to fire damage.

_ _/_ _/20_ _

Kenny's The Vesey Arms

7 Main Street, Lucan Village, Co Dublin
(1) 628 0248
information@kennysoflucan.com
www.kennysoflucan.com
A traditional local pub. 'Innkeeping with tradition.' It has been trading as Kenny's since 1969. Food is served every day and there is occasional entertainment.

_ _/_ _/20_ _

The Lord Lucan

Finnstown Shopping Centre, Newcastle Road, Lucan, Co Dublin, (1) 621 7100
lordlucan@indigo.ie, www.lordlucanpub.com
A traditional local pub, established in 1997. It was the Jedward fan club's home when they were on *The X Factor* in 2009, and the pub still follows their career. Food is served every day and there is regular entertainment.

_ _/_ _/20_ _

The Lucan County

Lucan Bypass, Lucan, Co Dublin
(1) 628 3075
Set in the grounds of the Spa Hotel this is a traditional local pub, very much into sport. Food is served every day and there is regular entertainment.

_ _/_ _/20_ _

O'Neill's Lucan Inn

Main Street, Lucan, Co Dublin
(1) 628 1497
A traditional local pub with regular entertainment.

_ _/_ _/20_ _

McEvoy's

Grand Canal, Hazelhatch, Co Dublin
(1) 628 8283
Set alongside the Grand Canal this traditional bar is also called The Workman Bar after a horse called Workman which was trained locally in Ringwood and won the Aintree Grand National in 1939. The pub, which was established in the early 1800s used to be an inn and was the first stop for boat traffic leaving Dublin. Canal boatmen lodged here and stabled their horses overnight. The pub draws a local crowd and is a stop-off for canal traffic.

_ _/_ _/20_ _

Muldowney's of Rathcoole

Main Street, Rathcoole, Co Dublin
(1) 458 9799
A traditional local pub established circa 1900. It has a large garden with a children's play area. Food is served every day and there is regular entertainment.

_ _/_ _/20_ _

Pavilion Lounge and Swift Bars

Citywest Hotel, Saggart, Co Dublin
(1) 401 0500
sales@citywesthotel.com
www.citywesthotel.com
Two bars housed in The Citywest Hotel. Food is served every day. A second hotel in the complex called The Golf Hotel, currently only used as an overflow hotel for large events, houses The Alexandra Bar.

_ _/_ _/20_ _

The Penny Hill

Ballyowen Road, Lucan, Co Dublin
(1) 621 4361
www.louisfitzgerald.com
A traditional local pub, established in 1999. Its name in Irish, An Cnoc Pingín, is displayed. Food is served every day and there is occasional entertainment. The pub is also home to Mint @ The Penny Hill Nightclub which opens on Wednesday, Friday and Saturday.

_ _/_ _/20_ _

The Rathcoole Inn

Main Street, Rathcoole, Co Dublin
(1) 458 9204
info@rathcooleinn.ie
www.rathcooleinn.ie
Famed as Ireland's oldest two-storey thatched public house this traditonal local pub was established in 1785. Food is served from Sunday to Friday and there is regular entertainment.

_ _/_ _/20_ _

The Woodquay Bar and The Cellar Bar

Finnstown Country House Hotel, Newcastle Road, Lucan, Co Dublin, (1) 601 0700
manager@finnstown-hotel.ie, www.finnstown-hotel.ie
The Woodquay Bar is a traditional bar in The Finnstown Country House Hotel. Food is served every day. There is regular entertainment in The Cellar Bar. The hotel also houses The Peacock Restaurant as well as keeping peacocks which patrol around the hotel.

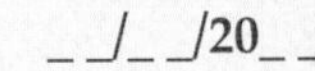
_ _/_ _/20_ _

Index

Symbols

A

B

C

D

H

I

J

K

L

M

N

O

P

Q

R

S

T

U

V

W

Y